DRAWN FROM PARADISE

DRAWN FROM PARADISE

The discovery, art and natural history of
the birds of paradise

David Attenborough and Errol Fuller

Collins

Dust Jacket: *End to the Squandering of Beauty* (detail). Raymond Ching, 2011. Oils on canvas.

Endpapers: King Bird of Paradise, coloured engraving by Paul Oudart, and Red Bird of Paradise, coloured engraving by Jean-Gabriel Prêtre, both from René Lesson's *Histoire Naturelle des Oiseaux de Paradis et des Epimaques* (1834–35).

Half title: Greater Bird of Paradise. Woodcut from Conrad Gesner's *Vogelbuch*, 1557.

Frontispiece: *Mr Thomson, Animal and Bird Preserver to the Leverian and British Museums* (detail). Ramsey Richard Reinagle, *c.*1800. Oils on canvas. Courtesy of The Yale Centre for British Art, Paul Mellon Collection, New Haven.

Facing page: Papuans hunting the Greater Bird of Paradise on the Aru Islands. Engraving by T. W. Wood for A. R. Wallace's celebrated book *The Malay Archipelago* (1869). The picture is misleading in that the plumes of the displaying birds are shown as if sprouting from above, instead of beneath the wings.

HarperCollins Publishers
77–85 Fulham Palace Road
London W6 8JB

www.harpercollins.co.uk

Collins is a registered trademark of HarperCollins Publishers Ltd.

First published in 2012

17 16 15 14 13 12
10 9 8 7 6 5 4 3 2 1

Designed by Errol Fuller

For HarperCollins
Publisher: Myles Archibald
Editor: Dr Jan McCann

A catalogue record for this book is available from the British Library.

ISBN 978-0-00-748761-5

Collins uses papers that are natural, renewable and recyclable products made from wood grown in sustainable forests. The manufacturing processes conform to the environmental regulations of the country of origin.

Printed and bound in Hong Kong by Printing Express

Nature seems to have taken every precaution that these, her choicest treasures, may not lose value by being too easily obtained. First we find an open, harbourless, inhospitable coast, exposed to the full swell of the Pacific Ocean; next, a rugged and mountainous country, covered with dense forests, offering in its swamps and precipices and serrated ridges an almost impassable barrier to the central regions; and lastly, a race of the most savage and ruthless character.... In such a country and among such a people are found these wonderful productions of nature. In those trackless wilds do they display that exquisite beauty and that marvellous development of plumage, calculated to excite admiration and astonishment among the most civilized and most intellectual races of man . . .

Alfred Russel Wallace. 'Narrative of Search after Birds of Paradise', *Proceedings of the Zoological Society of London* (1862).

(This page and facing page)

End to the Squandering of Beauty
(Entry of the Birds of Paradise into Western Thought).
Raymond Ching, August to December, 2011.
Oils on canvas, 180 cm x 240 cm (6 ft x 8 ft).

(Pages 8–19: details)

Thus one of my ... objects in coming to the far East was accomplished. I had obtained a specimen of the ...

The remote island in which I found myself situated, in an almost unvisited sea, far from the tracks of merchant-fleets; and novices the wild luxuriant tropical forests ... of Paradise ... on every side. I thought of the long ages of the past, during which the successive generations of this little creature had run their course — year by year ... melancholy ... should live out their lonely ... and exhibit their charm only in there wild inhospitable regions; doomed for ages yet to come to hopeless barbarism; while on the ... hand ... civilized ... should ... these wild inhospitable regions, deemed to all appearance such a wanton waste of beauty. Such ideas excite a feeling of melancholy. It seems sad that ... on the one hand ... ... if civilized man should ever reach these distant lands, and bring moral, intellectual, and practical ... to bear ... recesses of these virgin forests; we may be sure that he will so disturb the nicely-balanced ... should ... cause the disappearance, and finally the extinction, of these very beings whose wonderful structure and beauty ...

Paradisea apoda
Paradisea minor
Paradisea rubra
Paradisea regiana
Paradisea guilielmi
Schlegelia wilsoni
Paradisea decora
Paradisea raggiana
Paradisea guilielmi
Schlegelii melanoleuca
Paradisea rudolphi
Ptilotis ...
Astropia splendidissima
Astropia ...
Paradisea ...
Parotia sefilata
Parotia wahnesi
Parotia lawesii
Parotia carolae
Seleucidis melanoleuca
Ptiloris magnifica
Craspedophora ...
Diphyllodes magnificus
Cicinnurus regius
Cicinnurus magnificus
Pteridophora alberti

'Thus one of my objects in coming to the far East was accomplished. I had obtained the remote island in which I found myself situated, in an almost unvisited sea, far from the tracks of merchant-fleets and navies; the wild life with no intelligent eye to gaze upon their loveliness to all appearance such a wanton waste of beauty. Such ideas excite a feeling of melancholy. It seems sad that of the long ages of the past, during which the successive generations of this little creature had run their course - year by year of being born, and live out their lives and exhibit their charms only in these wild inhospitable regions, doomed for ages yet to come to hopeless barbarism; while on the ot we may be sure that he will so disturb the nicely-balance should and bring morals, intellectual and physical light into the recesses of these virgin forests, whose wonderful structure and beauty he along or the cause the disappearance and finally the extinction, of these very beings

'Thus one of my   objects in coming to the far East was accomplished. I ha

The remote island in which I found myself situated, in an almost unvisited sea, far from the tracks of merchant-fleets and navies; the
on every side; I thought of the long ages of the past, during which the successive generations of this little creature had run their course – year by year of
with no intelligent eye to gaze upon their loveliness to all appearance such a wanton waste of beauty. Such ideas excite a feeling of melancholy. It seems
should live out their lives and exhibit their charms only in these wild inhospitable regions, doomed for ages yet to come to hopeless barbarism; whi
and bring morals intellectual and physical light into the recesses of these virgin forests, we may be sure that he will so disturb the n
cause the disappearance and finally the extinction, of these very beings whose wonderful structure and beaut

...ed a specimen of the King Bird of Paradise...
...luxuriant tropical forest, which stretched far away
...rn, and living and dying amid these dark & gloomy woods,
...hat on the one hand such exquisite creatures
...other hand, should civilized man ever reach these distant
...nced relations of organic and inorganic nature
...fitted to appreciate and enjoy.

Paradisaea apoda

Paradisaea decora
Paradisaea raggiana
Paradisaea guilielmi
Seleucidis melanoleuca
Paradisaea rudolphi
Ptiloris magnificus
Astrapia splendissima
Epimachus
Epimachus
Epimachus
Astrapia nigra
stephaniae
Epimachus bruijnii
Parotia
Parotia rothschildi

Paradisaea

Paradisaea minor

Paradisaea apoda

Paradisaea decora

Paradisaea raggiana

Paradisaea guilielmi

Seleucidis melanoleuca

Paradisaea rudolphi

Ptiloris magnificus

Astrapia splendissima

Epimachus me...

Epimachus

Epimachus

Astra...

Collected by A.R. WALLACE 185...
Paradisea regis
♀ Aru Islands

Two or three [men of Aru, New Guinea] begged me for the twentieth time to tell them the name of my country. Then, as they could not pronounce it… they insisted I was deceiving them, that it was a name of my own invention. One old man… was… indignant. 'Ung-lung!' said he. 'Who ever heard of such a name? Ang lang, that can't be the name of your country' Then he tried to give a convincing illustration. 'My country is Wanumbai – anybody can say Wanumbai. But N-glung! Who ever heard of such a name? Do tell us the real name of your country… then when you are gone we shall know how to talk about you.' The whole party remained convinced I was deceiving them. They then attacked me on another point – what all the animals and birds… were preserved so carefully for. I tried to explain… that they would be stuffed, and made to look as if alive, and people in my country would go to look at them. But this was not satisfying; in my country there must be many better things to look at… They [the Aru men] did not want to look at them [the birds]; and we, who made calico and glass and knives, and all sorts of wonderful things, could not want things from Aru to look at…. The old man said to me, in a low, mysterious voice, 'What becomes of them when you go on to the sea?' 'Why, they are all packed up in boxes,' said I. 'What did you think became of them?' 'They all come to life again, don't they?' said he… and he kept repeating, with an air of deep conviction, 'Yes, they all come to life again, that's what they do – they all come to life again.'

Alfred Russel Wallace. *The Malay Archipelago* (1869).

'Thus one of my objects in coming to the far East was accomplished. I had obtained a specimen of the King

situated, in an almost unvisited sea, far from the tracks of merchant-fleets and navies; the wild luxuriant tropical forest, which stretched far away

during which the successive generations of this little creature had run their course — year by year of being born, and living and dying amid these dark & gloomy woods,

all appearance such a wanton waste of beauty. Such ideas excite a feeling of melancholy. It seems sad that on the one hand, should such exquisite creatures

only in these wild inhospitable regions, doomed for ages yet to come to hopeless barbarism; while on the other hand, these distant lands

the recesses of these virgin forests, we may be sure that he will so disturb the nicely-balanced relations of organic and inorganic nature as to

of these very beings whose wonderful structure and beauty he alone is fitted to appreciate and enjoy.

Bird of Paradise...'

(*Above*). Arfak Six-wired Bird of Paradise. John Latham, *c.* 1780. Watercolour (copied from an engraving by Pierre Sonnerat – *see* page 121), 15 cm x 12 cm (6 in x 5 in). The Natural History Museum, London.

(*Facing page*). John Gould with a specimen of Count Raggi's Bird of Paradise (for a more formal reproduction *see page 241*). H. R. Robertson, 1878. Oils on canvas. Private collection.

CONTENTS

Introduction

To the human eye, birds are among the most beautiful and intriguing of all nature's creations. Even a single stray feather, picked up by chance on a country walk, is a thing of wonder if examined closely. Its form, delicacy, and its colouring – sometimes subdued, sometimes gaudy – each have the power to astonish. And even the most familiar of species – the soberly dressed house sparrow or the common starling, for instance – are creatures of subtle beauty when viewed with fresh eyes.

There are, of course, whole families of birds well known for the astonishing visual impact of their plumage. Take, for example, the pheasant family. It boasts many spectacularly coloured species – the peacock, the tragopans and monals, or even the common pheasant itself – that defy description in words. Many other families contain kinds that are equally remarkable.

But one family stands out from the rest, not just because of the exquisite appearance of many of its species, but also because of the sheer extravagance of variety, colour and form that these creatures parade. These are birds that truly live up to their name: birds of paradise.

From the moment of their introduction to the European mind in the early sixteenth century, their unique beauty was recognised and commemorated in the first name that they were given; birds so beautiful must be birds from paradise! This naming extravaganza even continued into the nineteenth century when newly discovered species were named after illustrious crowned heads of Europe – Prince Rudolph's Blue Bird of Paradise, Princess Stephanie's Bird of Paradise, the Emperor of Germany's Bird of Paradise. The list of royal names goes on and on. Nor were splendid names enough to satisfy the inquiring minds of those who encountered the birds. In the early days all manner of fanciful stories and theories grew up to explain the mystery of their phenomenally beautiful appearance, and the tales quickly acquired mythical status. And as far as mystery is concerned, these birds are still wrapped in enigma.

(Facing page). Feathers from Paradise. Jacques Barraband, *c.*1802. Watercolour, 52 cm x 38 cm (21 in x 15 in). Private collection.

(*Above*). King Bird of Paradise, male. Jacques Barraband, *c.*1802.
Watercolour. 52 cm x 38 cm (21 in x 15 in).
Private collection.

(*Facing page*). Two male Black Sicklebills with a female.
Hand-coloured lithograph by William Hart from R. Bowdler
Sharpe's *Monograph of the Paradiseidae* (1891–98).

(*Overleaf*). Two species of plume bird, both males. Watercolours
by Jacques Barraband, *c.*1802, 52 cm x 38 cm (21 in x 15 in).
Private collection. (*Left*). Lesser Bird of Paradise. (*Right*). Red Bird
of Paradise.

Of course, we now know much more than the European scholars of the early sixteenth century who received the first specimens from the then remote lands somewhere far to the east. But there is much that is still unknown.

A major reason for this mystery surely lies in the nature of the birds' main homeland, the great island of New Guinea. Shrouded in exotic mystery, this island stronghold is one of the world's last truly wild places. Its jungle-covered mountain ranges and steamy, tangled lowlands provide some of the most formidable and daunting of terrains. Add to this the ferocious reputation of New Guinea's inhabitants, and the island has represented something of a fortress against exploration and industrial exploitation. In the coming decades this state of affairs will doubtless change, but for the time being much of the island remains in a virtually pristine state, and many bird of paradise secrets stay intact.

Most people with an interest in ornithology will recognise the gloriously plumed Greater Bird of Paradise, but to many it comes as something of a surprise to learn that this species is not alone. In fact, more than 40 distinct species are currently recognised. Among these are quite astounding differences in size, shape and colour patterning. The tiny King Bird of Paradise, for instance, with its exquisite red plumage, metallic green breast band and peculiar curled ends to the tail feathers (which are otherwise no more than naked quills), seems to have little in common with the metre-long Black Sicklebill sporting a shimmering tail and long, slender, down-curved beak. Yet all the species are bound together by underlying structural affinities.

These similarities are much more apparent in the females of the various species. Often these soberly plumaged birds (it is only the males of each species that are spectacularly adorned) are remarkably alike, even though their respective males look so very different.

The species generally referred to as plume birds are the ones that conform in appearance to general expectations. Characterised by great bunches of lace-like flank plumes coloured variously yellow, red, white or even blue, it is these species that provide the basis for the iconic images of birds of paradise that grace all manner of postage stamps and advertising campaigns.

The national airline of Papua New Guinea carries a plume bird as its logo, and advertisements for the country or its products rarely – if ever – appear without one. In fact, New Guinea is characterised by the image of the bird of paradise. Its national sport may be rugby league, its cultural heritage may be summed up in the dramatic masks and tribal artefacts made by the indigenous peoples, its image often reduced to photographs of tribesmen in spectacular costumes, but its most widely known residents are birds of paradise.

That this family of birds has always exerted a hold over the minds of humans is shown by the manner in which the peoples of New Guinea have prized them from time immemorial. Indeed, the very nature of their tribal customs is defined by the extravagant use of, and trade in, bird of paradise feathers.

Curiously, the production of ethnographical artefacts and works of art hardly reflects this great cultural interest – in traditional New Guinea tribal art there is little or nothing that uses the bird of paradise motif, at least in terms of sculpture or painting. It is a well-worn idea that art is often the product of the need to possess. An artist may paint a bird, a flower, a woman, a view, because he or she wants to own that image, to possess it. New Guinea tribesmen did, of course, own the actual birds themselves. Why would they need the help of art to facilitate that urge? They possessed the birds quite literally, and adorned themselves in the most fantastic ways with the feathers. Nor were they oblivious to the fundamental purpose of this extravagant ornamentation. When a New Guinea tribesman arrayed himself with gorgeous plumes and feathers, and danced, he too was displaying and advertising his sexual desirability.

(*Above*). *The Five Senses and the Four Elements* – an early representation of a Greater Bird of Paradise, painted using an imported dried skin as a model. Though seemingly wingless and legless, it is propelling itself through the open window – perhaps returning to paradise! Jacques Linard, 1627. Oils on canvas, 103 cm x 150 cm (41 in x 60 in). Musée des Beaux-Arts, Algiers.

(*Facing page*). Three females.
(*Top*). Queen Carola's Six-wired Bird of Paradise. Detail from a watercolour by William T. Cooper, *c*.1976.
(*Middle*). King Bird of Paradise. Detail from a hand-coloured lithograph by Joseph Wolf and Joseph Smit from D. G. Elliot's *Monograph of the Paradiseidae* (1873).
(*Bottom*). Magnificent Bird of Paradise. Detail from a watercolour by William T. Cooper, 1976.

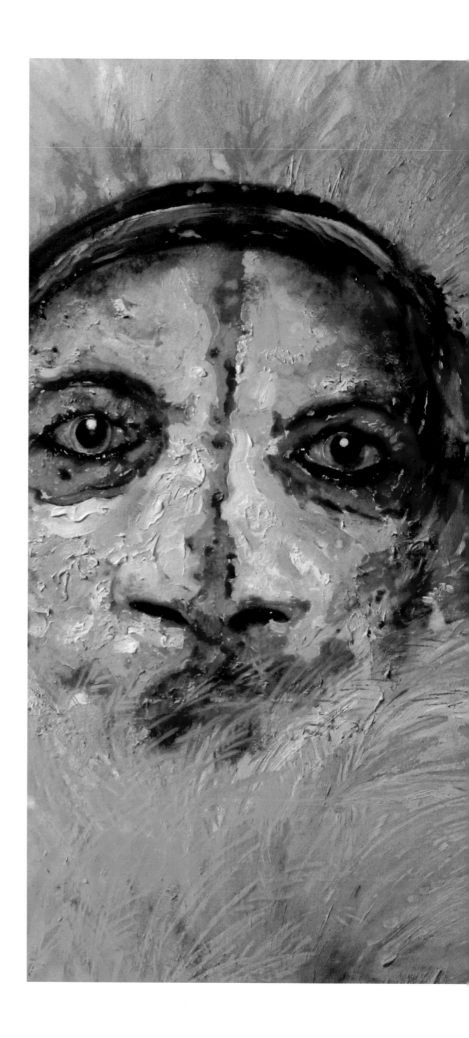

Paint and Plumes. Errol Fuller, 2012. Oils on panel,
46 cm x 66 cm (18 in x 26 in). Private collection.

(*Above*). Greater Bird of Paradise. Charles R. Knight. Oils on panel, size, date and whereabouts unknown. Copyright Rhoda Knight Kalt.

(*Facing page*). Male Lesser Birds of Paradise with a female. Hand-coloured lithograph by William Hart and John Gould from Gould's *Birds of New Guinea* (1875–88).

Once these same feathers reached the western world their impact was immediate. Here it manifested itself through art and fantastical stories and myths, while princes and emperors displayed power and taste by acquiring the rarely imported specimens for their cabinets of curiosities and museums. The impact may indeed have taken a more veiled, symbolised, form, but it was still profound and eventually led to a manner of human adornment strangely parallel to that shown among New Guinea peoples. Through the nineteenth century and on into the first decades of the twentieth, it was the very height of fashion to add the most bizarre concoctions of feathers as appendages to finely crafted hats and clothes. But this time it wasn't the males who were displaying their loveliness; it was the most fashionable of ladies!

In 1522 the first of many, many bird of paradise plumes arrived in Europe. Within just months they had attracted the attention of a celebrated artist, Hans Baldung Grien. His picture may be a comparatively flimsy affair (*see page 43*), but it began a tradition among artists that continues to this day. The list of artists who have felt compelled to draw or paint birds of paradise is studded with some illustrious names: Brueghel, Rubens, Rembrandt, Millais. Then there are men who actually specialised in painting birds: Barraband, Wolf, Hart, Gould, Keulemans. And, of course, there are modern painters. Walter Weber produced a series of iconic images for *The National Geographic Magazine* during the early 1950s, William T. Cooper illustrated two major monographs on birds of paradise, and Raymond Ching is known throughout the world for his poetic and highly charged paintings.

It is an inevitable consequence of a book that attempts to trace the history of these birds through their appearance in art, that the work of these few men will feature to what may seem a disproportionate degree. Many people have painted birds of paradise, but only a few have produced work that is worthy of particular attention, or has significantly added to the body of work that went before them. One reason for this (and it applies almost as much today as it did in past times) is that these birds are difficult to see. In days gone by it was virtually impossible, but even in the twenty-first century it is by no means easy. They rarely occur in zoos or aviaries, and a trip to New Guinea – daunting in itself – will not necessarily lead to seeing birds in ways that are helpful to the artist. Another reason is that these are extraordinarily difficult birds to capture in paint or pencil, even if good views are obtained. They do not always

(*Facing page*).
Eleven bird of paradise species from five distinct genera that lack the more extravagent features usually associated with the family.

(*Top row, from left*).
Paradise Crow (*Lycocorax pyrrhopterus*); Glossy-mantled Manucode (*Manucodia ater*); Long-tailed Paradigalla (*Paradigalla carunculata*); Crinkle-collared Manucode (*Manucodia chalybata*).
All images except Paradigalla hand-coloured lithographs by W. Hart from R. Bowdler Sharpe's *Monograph of the Paradiseidae* (1891–98). Paradigalla, watercolour by Lilian Medland from Tom Iredale's *Birds of Paradise and Bower Birds* (1950).

(*Middle row, from left*).
 Short-tailed Paradigalla (*Paradigalla brevicauda*), hand-coloured lithograph by H. Gronvold from *Ibis* (1912); Sickle-crested Bird of Paradise (*Cnemophilus macgregorii*); Curl-crested Manucode (*Manucodia comrii*), both images hand-coloured lithographs by W. Hart from R. Bowdler Sharpe's *Monograph of the Paradiseidae* (1891–98).

(Bottom row, from left).
Loria's Bird of Paradise (*Cnemophilus loriae*); Wattle-billed Bird of Paradise (*Loboparadisea sericea*); Jobi Manucode (*Manucodia jobiensis*); Trumpet Bird (*Manucodia keraudrenii*).
All images except Jobi Manucode hand-coloured lithographs by W. Hart from R. Bowdler Sharpe's *Monograph of the Paradiseidae* (1891–98). Jobi Manucode, watercolour by Lilian Medland from Tom Iredale's *Birds of Paradise and Bower Birds* (1950).

conform to the shapes that more familiar birds adopt, and making sense of the extravagant ornamental plumage – the metallic breast shields and throat gorgets, the axe-shaped feather fans, the lace-like plumes – is not an easy exercise.

This book is not a complete cultural history of the birds of paradise and their effect on man. It is focused very much through western eyes. The matter of the birds' influence on, and importance to, the peoples of New Guinea is only touched on: that is a subject for another book.

Nor does it include photographs, despite the fact that in recent years many wonderful images have been captured by camera. Photography, however, is beyond the scope of the present work, although it would make a splendid subject for another.

The book is certainly not intended as a complete monograph of the Paradiseidae, with each species described in detail. It is more in the nature of a tour through art and history with a good deal of ornithology thrown in. Its central idea is to showcase the breathtaking beauty of these birds and the enormous interest that surrounds them. As it is something of a historical ramble, the chapters are ordered according to the sequence in which the birds representing the various genera made their appearance in Europe.

According to generally accepted opinion, the species currently recognised are divided into sixteen genera, but only eleven of these genera are featured here in detail. The other five contain species – eleven of them – that are less visually spectacular and have histories that are, perhaps, less absorbing. They represent earlier stages in the evolutionary history of the bird of paradise family before the males abandoned their parental duties to devote themselves to the sexual displays that now dominate their lives and made them creatures of such extraordinary and extravagant beauty.

1

Paradisaea

The First of the Family –
the Plume Birds
Genus *Paradisaea*

The first specimens of birds of paradise to arrive in Europe looked very odd indeed. Several were unloaded from a small weather-beaten ship, *The Victoria,* that docked on 6 September 1522, in the little port of Sanlucar de Barrameda, 32 km (20 miles) north of Cadiz on the southwestern Atlantic coast of Spain, and close to Seville. That the shrivelled dried skins had once been birds was evident from the fact that they had beaks. But there was no skull in the skin of the head, the flattened feathered bodies were entirely empty, and there was no sign of wings or feet. Two strange wire-like quills projected from the tail, each about twice the length of the bird's body. But the most wonderful part of their anatomy was their plumes. Thick golden bunches sprouted from either side of the body. These plume feathers did not have barbs that link together into an air-catching vane like normal wing feathers. Instead, the barbs were thread-thin but rigid and widely separated, giving each feather a breath-taking gauzy delicacy. And the feathers were so long that lower down the body the two bunches amalgamated and extended far beyond the tail, had there been one, in a single glorious, golden cascade.

The Victoria was the only survivor of a small fleet of five ships that three years earlier had set out from Sanlucar, under the command of Ferdinand Magellan (1480–1521), in an attempt to reach the far distant Spice Islands, the small archipelago west of New Guinea that today is known as the Moluccas. Magellan planned to do so by sailing, not down the coast of Africa and then eastwards across the Indian Ocean as Portuguese rivals had done, but by heading west across the Atlantic, rounding the southern tip of South America for the very first time, and then crossing the vast emptiness of the Pacific. The expedition succeeded in doing so, but at great cost. It became embroiled in a local war in the Philippines and Magellan was killed. Four of the ships were lost – wrecked, burnt or so weather-beaten that they were abandoned. But *The Victoria* had survived and so became the first ship ever to circumnavigate the globe.

(*Facing page*). A Lesser Bird of Paradise painted from a wingless and footless specimen in the collection of Emperor Rudolf II. Joris or Jacob Hoefnagel, *c.*1600. Gouache on parchment, 36 cm x 27 cm (14 in x 11 in). National Library of Austria, Vienna.

(*Pages 36 and 37*). Greater Bird of Paradise (detail). Jacques Barraband, *c.*1802. Watercolour. For full image *see page 57.*

(*Facing page, top*). The first known European image of a bird of paradise. Silverpoint drawing by Hans Baldung Grien, 1522, 10 cm x 15 cm (4 in x 6 in). Statens Museum for Kunst, Copenhagen.

(*Facing page, centre*). The first known coloured image – painted on a page of the prayer book known as *The Farnese Hours* by Giulio Clovio, *c*.1540. Pierpont Morgan Library, New York.

(*Facing page, below*). Detail of Clovio's picture.

(*Pages 40 and 41*). Three early paintings of preserved skins of Greater Birds of Paradise.

(*Page 40, left*). Anonymous, *c*.1630. Watercolour and body colour, 23 cm x 9 cm (9½ in x 3½ in). Private collection.

(*Page 40, right*). Anonymous, sometimes attributed to Conrad Aichler, 1567. Watercolour and body colour, 45 cm x 22 cm (18 in x 8½ in). The significance of the inscription 'Meralda' is unknown, and the image bears some connection to the woodcut from Gesner's *Vogelbuch* of 1557 (*see the half title page*); the same preserved skin may have served as the model. The distorted shape of the head is due to Papuan methods of preservation – the skull was removed during the drying process. Staatliche Kunstsammlungen, Dresden.

(*Page 41*). Anonymous, *c*.1560. Watercolour and body colour, 59 cm x 37 cm (24 in x 15 in). Graphische Sammlung, University of Erlangen-Nuremberg.

Her crew had wonderful tales to tell – of new lands and new peoples, of Patagonian giants who quenched hunger by thrusting arrows down their throats so that they threw up their meals and could eat them again, of sea monsters that threatened their ship, and of gigantic birds so big they could pick up elephants in their talons. The shrivelled skins were proof of another marvel – birds that floated high in the skies beyond the sight of men. There they fed on dew, and were only found by humans when they died and fell to earth. That was why, as all could see, the skins lacked both wings and feet. The people in the Spice Islands called these wonderful creatures '*bolong diwata*', birds of the gods.

The skins had been presented to the expedition as a gift to the King of Spain by the Rajah of Bacan, one of the Spice Islands. But in truth neither the Rajah nor his people had any first-hand knowledge of the living birds. The specimens were brought to them by traders from lands far away to the east of their islands.

Most European artists and scholars seem to have accepted the stories about the birds' way of life at face value, although the first known European drawing of these extraordinary creatures is an unflattering but honest portrayal conveying little of the wonder that was so captivating. Produced in 1522, very soon after *The Victoria* landed, by a German artist, Hans Baldung Grien (1484/5–1545), the plumes are indicated by just a few simple parallel lines. The skins were certainly circulating quickly. By October 1522 the scribe of Charles V, Holy Roman Emperor, was writing to a bishop in Salzburg explaining that he had acquired for the emperor (from *The Victoria's* captain) the boneless body of a wonderful bird, 'so that he may delight in its rarity and splendour'.

A second picture, made some 20 years later, and this time in colour, gives more than a hint of the magical legends that still surrounded the birds. It was painted by a Croatian artist, Giulio Clovio (1498–1578) and appears in a small illuminated prayer book, now known as *The Farnese Hours*. Clovio clearly accepted the stories of the birds' connections with paradise, for he shows one sailing through the sky, trailing its plumes gloriously behind it, but without any sign of wings.

Even scholars and natural historians, whom one might have expected to be somewhat more critical, seem to have accepted the stories as truth. Ulysses Aldrovandus (1522–1605), in his great thirteen-volume encyclopaedia of natural history, which he started to publish in 1599, included illustrations of the bird drinking dew among the clouds.

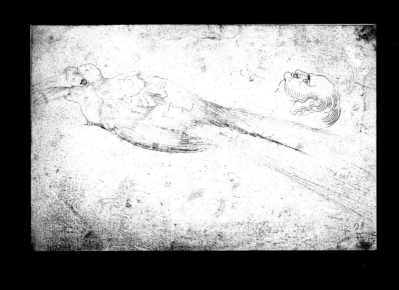

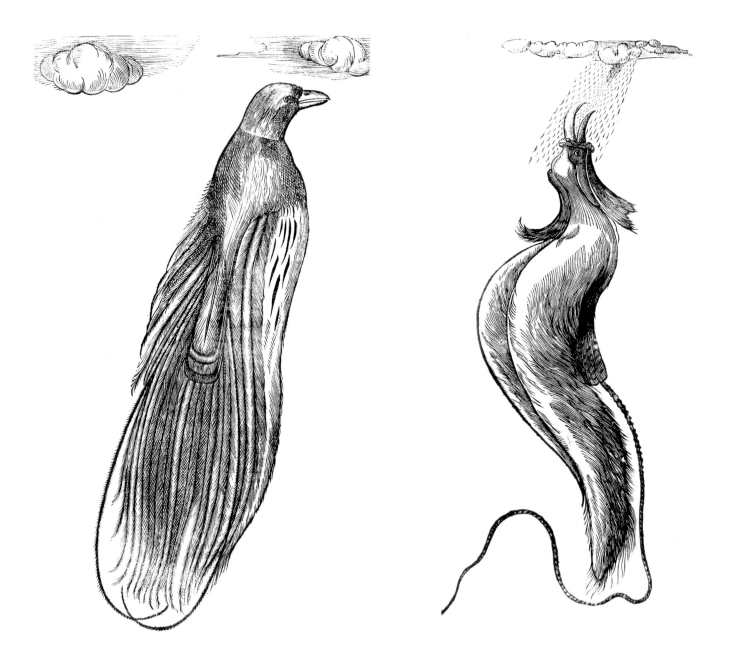

(*Facing page*). Two fanciful birds of paradise drinking dew from the clouds, both apparently wingless and footless. Woodcuts from Ulysses Aldrovandus' *Ornithologiae* (1599).

(*Above*). *The Garden of Eden*. Jan Brueghel the Elder, *c*.1617. Oils on oak panel,
53 cm x 84 cm (21 in x 33 in). Victoria and Albert Museum, London. A plumed bird of paradise
is perched on the thinnest branch in the top left corner, and another flies just beneath.

The Earthly Paradise and the Fall of Man. A collaboration between Peter Paul Rubens and Jan Brueghel the Elder, *c.*1617. Oils on panel, 78 cm x 112 cm (29 in x 45 in). Mauritshuis, The Hague.

Other authors, pondering on how such creatures could perpetuate themselves – as they must surely do since they are mortal and die – stated as a fact that the female laid her eggs on the male's back and then incubated them by sitting on both them and him as they sailed together through the sky. The wire-like quills projecting from the tail were also given a function. They, according to some accounts, were used as hooks with which the birds suspended themselves from the branches of trees when they wanted to rest from floating.

It was not until the seventeenth century that more rational ideas prevailed. *The Garden of Eden* was a popular subject for artists as it allowed them to paint pictures that had religious connections and yet also permitted the inclusion of images from the natural world. Jan Brueghel the Elder (1568–1625) produced one in which a bird of paradise perches on a branch – on two legs. Close by is a toucan and a macaw, and beneath them another bird of paradise in flight – with wings.

Brueghel also produced a picture, *The Earthly Paradise,* in collaboration with his Flemish countryman Peter Paul Rubens (1577–1640). Rubens is said to have painted the human figures, the horse, and the serpent in its tree, while Brueghel produced the rest. And on the ground stands a bird of paradise complete with wings and legs. Another flies to the left of the ostrich's head. At last birds of paradise were being portrayed un-mutilated, as real birds. Nonetheless, even after Brueghel, legions of other artists continued to show birds of paradise magically floating across the sky with their plumes streaming behind them – unconcealed by wings.

Concert of the Birds. Frans Snyders, 1629–30. Oils on canvas, 98 cm x 137 cm (38 in x 54 in). Many pictures with this title were produced by northern artists during the seventeenth and eighteenth centuries. They nearly all show an owl in the centre holding up a sheet of music surrounded by other birds, open-beaked, singing in chorus. Doubtless, they were inspired by the common sight in the countryside of an owl that dared to perch out in the open during daylight being mobbed by other smaller birds. Those shown here are all European with the exception of a South American parrot on the right and a Greater Bird of Paradise, with somewhat faded and dusty plumes, on the left. The score held by the owl seems to make no musical sense but that, perhaps, is of little consequence, since nearly all the birds shown have extremely discordant voices. Museo del Prado, Madrid.

As the decades passed, more and more of these extraordinary skins began to appear. They all came from the great 1,600 km (1,000 mile)-long island of New Guinea, lying north of Australia, or from its outlying archipelagos. From there they were traded right along the Indonesian island chain and into the mainland of Southeast Asia. Some went even further into the Himalayas to become part of the regalia of the Kings of Nepal, which they still are. They even reached Britain. A certain amount of evidence suggests that bird of paradise plumes were found among the personal possessions of Henry VIII after his death. The evidence that the ill-fated young Scottish prince who would become Charles I of England also possessed them is beyond question. About the year 1610 he posed for his portrait standing beside a table upon which he has placed a sumptuous fur hat with, pinned to it by a brooch, the preserved skin of a bird of paradise complete with plumes.

Just under 30 years later, Rembrandt van Rijn (1606–69) felt compelled to draw two specimens that, presumably, he had just acquired from a Dutch trading vessel, recently arrived from the East Indies. Rembrandt is known to have delighted in the rare and the curious, and such tastes were among the weaknesses that eventually led him into bankruptcy. When his goods were finally impounded and inventoried by bailiffs, a bird of paradise skin was listed among them.

The birds brought back by Magellan's men had in life – as well as gauzy plumes – yellow heads, bibs of rippling iridescent green, and brown bodies. Grien's drawing doesn't show quite enough detail positively to establish that they were Greater Birds of Paradise, although there are good grounds for supposing that they were. But there are, in fact, half a dozen species that fit the description. Carl Linnaeus (1707–78), the great Swedish cataloguer of the natural world, invented a generic name for them, *Paradisaea*. To the biggest of them, he added, no doubt with his tongue in his cheek, the specific name – *apoda*, meaning 'without feet'. A second species, the Lesser Bird (*Paradisaea minor*), also has golden plumes but is slightly smaller and lacks a small brown feathery cushion that the Greater Bird wears on his chest. The yellow plumes have a tendency to fade dramatically in preserved specimens, which is why many artists, using such specimens as reference, have shown them as white.

(*Facing page*). The boy who would grow up to be Charles I, King of England, with a sword hilt in his left hand and a hat decorated with the skin of a bird of paradise behind him. Robert Peake, *c*.1610. Oils on canvas, 127cm x 85 cm (66 in x 34 in). Scottish National Portrait Gallery, Edinburgh.

Three other species, the Red Bird (*P. rubra*), Count Raggi's Bird (*P. raggiana*) and Goldie's Bird (*P. decora*), are somewhat similar but have plumes that are not yellow but red. A sixth, the Emperor of Germany's Bird (*P. guilielmi*), which is restricted to a small patch of mountains near the eastern tip of the island, has genuinely white plumes that are even more lace-like than those of its relatives. It is only the males of each species that develop these ravishing plumes. The females are comparatively drab – brown above, somewhat paler beneath and often quite difficult to tell apart.

(*This page*). Two birds of paradise. Rembrandt van Rijn, *c*.1640. Pen and bistre with wash and white body colour, 18 cm x 15 cm (7 in x 6 in). The Louvre, Paris.

(*Facing page*). Six species of plumed birds of paradise.

(*Top, left*). Count Raggi's Bird of Paradise – the first known illustration. Hand-coloured lithograph by Joseph Wolf and Joseph Smit from D. G. Elliot's *Monograph of the Paradiseidae* (1873).

(*Top, middle*). The Emperor of Germany's Bird of Paradise, male and female. Watercolour by William Cooper, *c*.1976, 60 cm x 47 cm (24 in x 17 in).

(*Top, right*). Greater Bird of Paradise, male. Engraving after a watercolour by Jacques Barraband from François Levaillant's *Histoire Naturelle des Oiseaux de Paradis* (1801–06). Also *see page 57.*

(*Bottom, left*). Goldie's Bird of Paradise, male and immature male. Hand-coloured lithograph by William Hart and John Gould from Gould's *Birds of New Guinea* (1875–88).

(*Bottom, middle*). The Red Bird of Paradise. Engraved plate, printed in colours and finished by hand by Jean Baptiste Audebert, from Audebert and Vieillot's *Oiseaux Dorés ou a reflets Metalliques* (1802).

(*Bottom, right*). Lesser Bird of Paradise, male and female. Watercolour by William Cooper, *c*.1976, 60 cm x 47 cm (24 in x 17 in).

Le grand Oiseau de Paradis emeraude, male

Le Paradis rouge Pl. 5

Something of the wonder and curiosity that was inspired in naturalists by the arrival of bird specimens in Europe is captured in a painting by Ramsey Richard Reinagle (1775–1862). Painted around 1800, it shows a taxidermist examining the skin of a plumed bird of paradise newly arrived from foreign parts, with an Argus Pheasant lying on the table beside him. Some controversy exists over the identity of the man in the painting. An old inscription on the reverse identifies him as 'Mr Thomson, animal and bird preserver to the Leverian and British Museums', but during recent decades the picture has been listed as a portrait of the celebrated English ornithologist John Latham (1740–1837). That this identification is incorrect is shown by the presence of a Lyrebird specimen hanging on the rear wall. Lyrebirds did not arrive in England from Australia until around 1800, by which time Latham would have been 60 years old. The most likely interpretation of the painting is that it shows the otherwise unknown Mr Thomson inspecting the recent arrival and considering its suitability for proper stuffing.

The Greater and the Lesser Birds were both portrayed in one of the first of the spectacular folio books that deal with the birds of paradise. It was written by the French zoologist Francois Levaillant (1753–1824) and published in 1806. Its great distinction lies in its plates, which were drawn by one of the finest of all bird artists, Jacques Barraband (1767–1809), who had the most extraordinary ability to represent the many different textures that feathers may have. Until the last decades of the twentieth century, his ornithological reputation rested largely on these engraved hand-coloured plates. But they give little hint of Barraband's true talent. The exquisite watercolours on which the engravings were based were almost entirely unknown. They had been acquired privately soon after they were painted and had remained in private possession, carefully preserved in albums that have protected them from fading ever since. It was only during the 1980s that the collection was split up and the full beauty and accuracy of the artist's work was revealed to the world.

But Barraband, like all his predecessors and those that followed him in the next few decades, had to work from skins. Consequently, their interpretations were, at best, inaccurate and often downright wrong. But then no European explorer travelling through New Guinea had even seen the living birds in the wild. The first to do that was a French traveller, René Primevère Lesson (1794–1849). He was serving on board a corvette, *La Coquille*, as the ship's naturalist with the explicit task of collecting

Mr Thomson, Animal and Bird Preserver to the Leverian and British Museums. Ramsey Richard Reinagle, *c.*1800. Oils on canvas, 147 cm x 147 cm (58 in x 58 in). Courtesy of The Yale Centre for British Art, Paul Mellon Collection, New Haven.

(*Previous two pages*). Two watercolours by Jacques Barraband, *c.*1800.

(*Left*). An immature male Lesser Bird of Paradise. 52 cm x 38 cm (21 in x 15 in).

(*Right*). Greater Bird of Paradise. 52 cm x 38 cm (21 in x 15 in). This painting was used as the basis for an engraved plate (*see page 53*), printed in colours and finished by hand in Levaillant's *Histoire Naturelle des Oiseaux de Paradis et des Rolliers* (1801–06).

(*This page*). Red Bird of Paradise, male, one of the species that Alfred Russel Wallace encountred during his travels in New Guinea and its surrounding islands. This engraving by T. W. Wood was one of a number of pictures produced for the celebrated book that Wallace published on his return to Britain, *The Malay Archipelago* (1869). A curiosity of this particular species is the structure of the two long central tail feathers. In other birds of the genus these resemble thin wires, but when examined closely those of the Red Bird are more like straps of plastic.

zoological specimens. Going ashore in July 1824 at Dorey Harbour, today's Manokwari, at the western end of New Guinea, he glimpsed one of the birds. 'Whilst we were walking very carefully on a wild pig trail through the dense scrub,' he wrote, 'suddenly in a slight curve a bird of paradise flew gracefully over our heads; trailing light like a meteor. We were so amazed,' he added, 'that the flintlocks in our hands did not move.'

Eventually, however, he did shoot specimens which were brought back to Europe and duly described in his book, the first treatise to be devoted to birds of paradise by someone who had actually seen living specimens. It is illustrated by several rather undistinguished (although charming) plates, drawn by French artists Paul Oudart (1796–*c.*1860) and Jean-Gabriel Prêtre (fl. 1800–50).

But even Lesson did not see the birds in display. The first European to do that was an Englishman, Alfred Russel Wallace (1823–1913). He was a self-educated man of limited means, but with a passion for natural history and a burning ambition to see nature at its most varied and wonderful in the tropics. He planned to pay for his journey there by collecting natural history specimens and selling them to museums and wealthy collectors. His first journey to the Amazon had ended in disaster when, after four years of arduous travel and industrious collecting, he started on the return journey to Britain. Three weeks out to sea, his ship caught fire and he lost thousands of carefully prepared specimens and all his meticulous field notes. He was lucky to escape with his life. When he at last reached Britain, nothing daunted, he made preparations for another expedition. This time, he decided to go to New Guinea, expressly to search for birds of paradise.

Landing in Singapore, he started a series of journeys travelling from island to island in local craft, and living often in conditions of great hardship. Eventually, he reached the Aru Islands that lie south of the western tip of New Guinea and established himself in the trading village of Dobbo. Here men came from all over south-east Asia to obtain bird of paradise skins that were still being prepared in the same way as in Magellan's time. And eventually, by following the hunters into the forest, Wallace found a tree in which Greater Birds were displaying. This is how he described the scene:

> The birds now commenced what people here call their '*sicaleli*'
> or dancing parties, in certain trees in the forest… which have

an immense head of spreading branches and large but scattered leaves, giving a clear space for the birds to play and exhibit their plumes. On one of these trees a dozen or twenty full-plumaged male birds assemble together, raise up their wings, stretch out their necks, and elevate their exquisite plumes, keeping them in a continual vibration. Between whiles they fly across from branch to branch in great excitement, so that the whole tree is filled with waving plumes in every variety of attitude and motion. At the time of [the bird's] excitement, the wings are raised vertically over the back, the head is bent down and stretched out, and the long plumes are raised up and expanded till they form two magnificent golden fans, striped with deep red at the base and fading off into the pale brown tint of the finely divided and softly waving points. The whole bird is then overshadowed by them, the crouching body, yellow head and emerald green throat forming but the foundation and setting to the golden glory which waves above. When seen in this attitude, the Bird of Paradise really deserves its name, and must be ranked as one of the most beautiful and wonderful of living things.

This, published in 1869, is the first account of the display of any bird of paradise and it could have been a good guide for anyone who tried to portray the dance of any species in the genus *Paradisaea*. Four years after it appeared, a wealthy American ornithologist, Daniel Giraud Elliot (1835–1915), published a huge book on the family, measuring 61 cm by 48 cm (24 in by 19 in), with plates drawn by Joseph Wolf (1820–99), a German artist who had settled in London. Wolf was already recognised as one of the great zoological artists of his time, whose pictures not only brought splendour to scientific publications but, on occasion, were hung in London's Royal Academy of Arts. He must surely have known of Wallace's description, for the book he illustrated for Elliot is dedicated to Wallace. Even so, the individual that dominates his plate of the Greater Bird is shown with relaxed plumes. Only in the distance and on a much smaller scale does he portray the display posture, and then he does so rather hesitantly – and inaccurately.

Greater Birds of Paradise, two males and a female. Hand-coloured lithograph by Joseph Wolf and Joseph Smit from D. G. Elliot's *Monograph of the Paradiseidae* (1873).

J. Wolf. & J. Smit del. et lith.

PARADISEA APODA.

He was bolder with his picture of the Lesser Bird. This plate is certainly one of the glories of Elliot's book, and it shows the bird with plumes erect in a spectacular haze that extends to the very margins of the huge plate. Glorious though it is, it too in its details fails to match Wallace's description.

Strangely, when in 1869 Wallace himself published his much delayed account of his travels, the artist T.W. Wood, who was given the task of providing the illustrations, also failed to show the birds' display posture correctly (see page 5), and makes it appear that the plumes sprout from above rather than beneath the wings. It seems very odd that such an accurate and meticulous observer as Wallace did not correct him.

In the year 1874, the challenge was taken up by the most famous ornithological publisher of his time, John Gould. (1804 – 1881). Gould had started his scientific career with the Zoological Society of London, where as taxidermist he had the responsibility of preserving the mortal remains of the rare animals that died in the Society's Gardens, the London Zoo. In 1830, he had published a set of illustrations based on a collection of bird skins that had been sent to the Society by a collector working in the Himalayas. It proved to be a great success and it set the pattern for the publications which occupied him for the rest of his life.

Each work Gould produced was issued in parts, each part containing a dozen or so plates accompanied by a scientific text written by Gould himself. The plates were spectacular, approximately 55 cm tall and 37 cm wide (22 inches x 14 inches), and each species had a plate to itself. Gould himself had little talent as an artist but in most cases he would make a rough sketch showing the composition he had in mind which he gave to an artist. Initially this was his wife, but after her untimely death he engaged a succession of specialist ornithological illustrators. Each had the difficult and highly specialised task of deducing from a dried feathered skin what the bird must have looked like in life. The drawing was then transferred to lithographic stone, either by the original artist or by a draughtsman specialising in such work, and from this an edition of several hundred black and white copies were printed. Each print was then coloured individually by hand to match the original drawing.

The parts, each with its dozen or so plates, were then sent to subscribers over a period that sometimes extended for several years before the entire work was complete. Often, Gould would add new parts to the number listed in his prospectus, as new species were discovered

Lesser Birds of Paradise, male and female. Hand coloured lithograph by Joseph Wolf and Joseph Smit from D. G. Elliot's *Monograph of the Paradiseidae* (1873).

PARADISEA MINOR

(*Above*). Lesser Birds of Paradise, males. William Hart, *c*.1875. Oils on canvas, 34 cm x 24 cm (13½ in x 9½ in). Private collection.

(*Right*). Goldie's Bird of Paradise, male and immature male. William Hart, *c*.1875. Oils on canvas, 34 cm x 24 cm (13½ in x 9½ in). Private collection.

Sometimes, he would start on a completely new project before its predecessor was finished. His Himalayan Birds were followed by *The Birds of Europe*. Then came a survey of the toucan family and another of trogons. After that he tackled *The Birds of Australia* and started on yet another long-running series devoted to hummingbirds. And in 1875 he began work on *The Birds of New Guinea* and engaged as one of the primary artists, an Irish-men, William Hart, (1830–1908) who had already worked on several of his previous volumes.

At least two of Hart's oil studies survive. One of these shows Goldie's Bird, which has red plumes and the artist, perhaps becoming confused by the illustration in Wallace's own book, shows them, incorrectly, as being erected beneath the wings rather than being raised above them.

The subject of the other study, a Lesser Bird, is apparently in display but also shows the plumes incorrectly raised and they droop rather limply instead of trembling as Wallace so vividly describes.

Maybe Wallace commented on these attempts, for by now he was well settled in Britain and in touch with London's circle of naturalists and scientists. Whether he did or not, the plate of the Lesser Bird that Hart eventually produced for Gould (*see page* 33) is a great improvement. It shows the bird in almost a correct display posture – tail depressed, wings erect, with its plumes raised above its back, and squawking vigorously.

But it was left to William Cooper, in 1977, illustrating a monograph written by Joseph Forshaw, to finally produce a truly accurate picture of one of these Paradisea species at the height of its ecstasy. The species in

(*Below*). *Still life with Sword, Velvet and Lesser Bird of Paradise.* Dirk de Bray, 1672. Oils on canvas, 37 cm x 52 cm (15 in x 21 in). Private collection.

(*Facing page*). Count Raggi's Bird of Paradise, male and female. William T. Cooper. Watercolour, produced for the dust wrapper of Cooper and Forshaw's book *The Birds of Paradise and Bower Birds* (1977), 60 cm x 42 cm (24 in x 17 in).

(*This page*). Lesser Bird of Paradise, with plumes of exaggerated length. Wilhelm Kuhnert. Oils on canvas, *c.*1900. Size and whereabouts unknown.

question is the red-plumed Count Raggi's Bird, and Cooper's painting, used on the dust wrapper of his book, shows – in exquisite detail – a male, head lowered beneath the branch on which it perches, displaying his magnificent plumes in a great scarlet fountain above his back, while a female watches critically.

But one species in the genus stands apart from the other six. It does not have a golden head or an iridescent bib like all the others in the genus. Instead its head and body are a comparatively sober black. But its wing feathers and its plumes are blue, pale on its wings and intense in its plumes. And yet on their reverse side these same plumes are coloured

rust red. Indeed, the species is so different that some authorities believe it should be given a genus of its own. It was discovered in 1884 by the German explorer Carl Hunstein in the then little-explored mountain range that runs down the centre of eastern New Guinea. Hunstein sent this specimen to another ornithologist, Otto Finsch, who duly named it *Paradisaea rudolphi* after Crown Prince Rudolf of Austria. In Finsch's ingratiating dedication he described the Prince as 'the high and mighty protector of ornithological researchers over the entire world'. Sadly the prince was to become rather more famous a few years later for dying in a suicide pact with his lover at a hunting lodge at Mayerling.

By the time of this species' discovery, John Gould was dead and his book on New Guinea birds had been completed by his friend Richard Bowdler Sharpe (1847–1909), who was in charge of ornithology at London's Natural History Museum. But so many new species of birds of paradise had now been identified that Sharpe took on another task – to publish a work devoted exclusively to the family (together with the bowerbirds that were then thought to be closely related). Many of the plates were taken from Gould's earlier work. Some were redrawn, and new plates of the latest discoveries were added, drawn once again by William Hart. Among these was the Blue Bird.

It is one of Hart's more awkward compositions. The male stands on a branch above the female, feathers fanned out to either side, breast shield extended with a slightly wider, darker fan beneath and a pair of long, ribbon-like wires tipped with small blue discs, extending downwards. Clearly Hart was attempting to show the male in display, but he could hardly have posed the bird in a more inaccurate way. He can scarcely be blamed because the male Blue Bird, when he attempts to attract a female, puts on one of the most improbable performances of the entire family.

Unlike all the rest of the *Paradisaea* genus, the male does not display alongside others. Instead, each has his own display perch in the forest, a gently sloping branch usually within a metre or so of the ground. The owner arrives in the early morning, often alighting high in the canopy above, and calls to announce his forthcoming performance. Then he descends to his perch. Holding tight with his toes, he slowly swings backwards until he is hanging upside down and facing in the opposite direction. Now he expands his plumes so that they form a shimmering triangular fan that covers almost his entire body with its point beneath his neck. The two wires in his tail, now pointing upwards, fall in an arc on either side.

(*This page*). Male Prince Rudolph's Blue Bird showing the surprising rust colour on the reverse of the blue plumes. Errol Fuller, 1994. Oils on panel, 40 cm x 25 cm (16 in x 10 in).

(*Facing page*). Male and female Blue Birds. Hand-coloured lithograph by William Hart from R. Bowdler Sharpe's *Monograph of the Paradiseidae* (1891–98).

PARADISORNIS RUDOLPHI, *Finsch.*

He begins to call, narrowing his white-lidded eyes until they are almost shut. As he does so he expands a patch of black feathers, rimmed with a rusty red on the edge near his feet. This now begins to pulse. With each expansion, a horizontal wave of shimmering ultramarine ripples upwards across the fan. And then he sings – if the sound he makes can be called a song. It is best described, perhaps, as an electronic buzzing interspersed with the shaking shuffle of maracas and a few random croaks, and it is unlike any other sound that comes from a bird's throat.

The Australian artist William Cooper is one of the few painters who has attempted to portray this almost unbelievable dance, and he does so superbly. One suspects, however, that had William Hart or any other nineteenth-century artist tried to paint a picture of this surreal performance, his viewers would have regarded it as just as fanciful and improbable as they regarded Aldrovandus' version showing the birds wingless and legless and floating in paradise.

Male Prince Rudolph's Blue Bird of Paradise displaying to a female. William Cooper, c.1990. Acrylic on panel, 76 cm x 114 cm (30 in x 45 in). Private collection.

William T. Cooper

2

Seleucidis

The Twelve-wired
Bird of Paradise
Genus *Seleucidis*

The second distinct kind of bird of paradise to arrive in Europe, of which we have any record, is a very odd one, the Twelve-wired. Indeed, it is so odd that many might be surprised to know that it even belongs to the bird of paradise family at all. But to hunters collecting plumes in the forest of New Guinea, plumes are plumes. And plumes it has.

They sprout from the male's flanks and are the same golden colour as the hunters' usual quarry, the Greater and Lesser species. And they are unquestionably plumes, for the barbs on either side of each quill do not zip together like flight feathers and are nothing more than gauzy filaments. But they are not erectile and each bunch contains six that are twice the length of the rest. In their lower sections, which are buried within the rest of the plumes, these strange feathers are white and fringed on either side with very short barbs. But where they extend beyond the main bunch they are no more than thin naked quills which are a shiny jet black. These are the wires that give the species its name.

Doubtless the golden plumes were enough to attract hunters in New Guinea and persuade oriental traders to accept the skins, perhaps at a lower price, as second-best birds of paradise. At any rate, at the end of the sixteenth century, one example found its way across Asia and Europe and into that cabinet of curiosities assembled by the Holy Roman Emperor Rudolf II (1552–1612) and kept at his castle in Prague.

Around the year 1600, he commissioned artists to produce a series of paintings of animals and birds living in his menagerie, and also of

(*Facing page*). Two adult male Twelve-wired Birds of Paradise. William Hart and John Gould. Hand-coloured lithograph from Gould's *Birds of New Guinea* (1875–88).

(*Pages 72 and 73*). Twelve-wired Birds of Paradise (details). Joseph Wolf. Hand-coloured lithograph from D. G. Elliot's *Monograph of the Paradiseidae* (1873). For full image *see page 85*.

interesting specimens from his curiosity collection. Acting on the royal instruction, Dutch artist Joris Hoefnagel (1542–1601), or perhaps his son Jacob (1575–c.1630), painted a picture of the Twelve-wired.

The specimen must have arrived in Europe only recently, for the artist shows the colour of its flank plumes as bright yellow and – as we now know – they always fade to white after a few years. Indeed, they do so even in live captive specimens if they are not given pandanus nuts in their food. The emperor's specimen, nonetheless, was clearly badly mangled. Its neck seems to have lost some of its feathers, for it is very scrawny, and instead of twelve wires, the bird has only ten, five on each side. That at least is understandable, for the wires, the quills, can become very brittle with age. Its other disfigurements, however, may have been inflicted by the native hunters who collected the specimen in New Guinea and treated it in the same way as other more famous species, the Greater and the Lesser, cutting off its wings and feet in order to emphasise the splendour of its similarly coloured golden flank plumes, and removing the skull to make preservation of the skin and feathers easier. Certainly there are no signs of either wings or feet in the painting, and the bird's body and tail appear to be little more than a black tube with a clump of golden plumes flaring on either side like the engines of a jet aircraft.

It is easy to sympathise with the predicament Hoefnagel faced when he came to paint his picture. After all, he was confronted with a dried relic bearing only a passing resemblance to the creature in life, and he had, of course, never had the opportunity of seeing a living individual. Furthermore, birds of paradise – with their often peculiar arrangement of plumes, fans and wires – hardly conform to the morphological patterns shown in more familiar birds.

Perhaps because the illustrations Rudolf commissioned remained the private property of the Habsburgs, the painting was long overlooked by naturalists, and the Twelve-wired remained largely unknown in Europe. Even the great Carl Linnaeus failed to give it a scientific name in the 1758 edition of his *Systema Naturae*.

A Twelve-wired Bird with a Scarlet Ibis below. Joris or Jacob Hoefnagel, c.1600. Gouache on parchment, 36 cm x 27 cm (14 in x 11 in). National Library of Austria, Vienna.

Twelve-wired Bird of Paradise, painted soon after François Daudin scientifically described the species, and showing the faded plumes on which he based his description. Jean-Gabriel Prêtre, *c*.1810. Watercolour on paper, 52 cm x 38 cm (21 in x 15 in). Private collection.

It wasn't until the year 1800, some two hundred years after Hoefnagel painted it, that the Twelve-wired was named scientifically and registered as an accredited member of the Bird of Paradise family. Then a French naturalist, François Daudin (1774–1804), a man who took up zoology despite the fact that his legs had been paralysed by a childhood disease, published a description of it. He recognised that although it was indeed a bird of paradise it was sufficiently different from any other species to be given a genus of its own. Searching, perhaps, for a name that might reflect its paradisal connections, he called it *Seleucidis*, a word used by the Greeks in classical times for migrant birds that appeared from nowhere – perhaps even paradise – and ate the locusts that threatened their crops. This might be considered to be a little over-imaginative, but the specific name he chose – *melanoleuca* – was even less suitable, for that word means 'black and white'. Clearly the particular specimen that he examined was an ancient one, the plumes of which had already faded.

In the years that followed, European artists who had the job of imagining how the bird appeared in the exotic forests on the other side of the world, made a somewhat better job of it than Hoefnagel. But they were all baffled by the twelve naked quills, the wires.

Just a year after Daudin had described the species, François Levaillant began to publish the first systematic catalogue of the bird of paradise family. It took him five years to complete, and the book's success rests largely on the illustrations engraved after watercolours produced by the incomparable Jacques Barraband (1767–1809), an artist who was second to none in capturing the exquisitely coloured plumage of tropical birds, whether they were parrots, toucans, cotingas or birds of paradise. Barraband's remarkably detailed pictures cannot be doubted in terms of the accuracy of these details. There is little question that he was using stuffed birds as models, and in some senses his paintings can be regarded as belonging to the genre of still life. They are crystal-clear depictions of the objects that lay before him, and because most of his watercolours were preserved for almost two centuries in albums well away from the fading caused by exposure to light, they remain in pristine condition.

Barraband called the Twelve-wired *Le Nebuleux*, a word that can mean either 'obscure' or 'hazy'. Perhaps he had the second meaning in mind because he shows the displaying male bird with his flank plumes in a great cloud above his back, with the wires projecting below

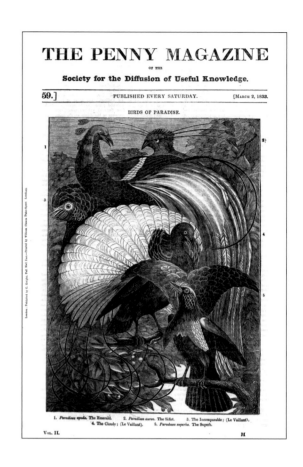

(This page, top left, and facing page). Two enigmatic images of birds that resemble Twelve-wired Birds of Paradise. Jacques Barraband, *c.*1800. Watercolour on paper, 52 cm x 38 cm (21 in x 15 in). Private collection.

(This page, top right). The cover of *The Penny Magazine* for 2 March 1833, one of many illustrations that leaned heavily on the work of Jacques Barraband.

symmetrically arranged like the extravagant curlicues and flourishes drawn by a practised calligrapher.

But there is a problem. Barraband produced two pictures and they show birds in different attitudes, but with exactly the same plumage features. But do they indeed show the Twelve-wired species? In fact, only ten wires are depicted in each image. This is easily explainable. It might well be that, like Hoefnagel's specimen, a couple of them had broken off.

More seriously, however, the bird's under-parts, which in life are white, are shown as black, the wings brown instead of black, and the beak entirely straight and thin, rather than showing the strong downward curve that is typical of the species. As the rest of his work shows, Barraband was meticulously accurate and it seems unlikely that he would have deliberately misrepresented the specimen from which he was working.

Was it perhaps incomplete and he had to imagine what the hinder part of its belly and the beak were like? Or maybe the specimen was in fact a hybrid, with a parent from a black-bellied species such as a Riflebird, hybridisation being not uncommon among members of the family. His two pictures, at any rate, remain somewhat problematic, even apart from the elegant posture of the bird's decorations.

Nouvelles Archives du Muséum 3ᵉ Série

Mémoires T. IV. Pl. 15.

Craspedophora Mantoui (Oust.)

St͏ᵉ des Imp. Lemercier, Paris

Mantou's Bird of Paradise, a hybrid between the Twelve-wired and the Magnificent Riflebird. J. G. Keulemans. Hand-coloured lithograph from *Nouvelle Archives du Museum, Paris* (1892).

To add even more mystery, an actual hybrid between the Riflebird and the Twelve-wired (and defined as such by plumage similarities) was recorded almost a century later, but it looks nothing like the bird painted by Barraband. A beautiful lithograph by the celebrated ornithological illustrator J. G. Keulemans (1842–1912) shows it has no close connection.

(*Below*). Male Twelve-wired Bird of Paradise. Artist unknown, but probably Sarah Stone, *c.*1800. Watercolour on paper, 25 cm x 30 cm (14 in x 12 in). Private collection.

Whatever the truth about Barraband's two enigmatic paintings, his influence – through his engravings rather than the original watercolours – persisted during the first few decades of the nineteenth century, and his work was regularly plagiarised in books, popular magazines and journals.

A picture dating from around the same time as Barraband's, illustrates a specimen in perhaps a more literal way. It may have been made by Sarah Stone (1760–1844), an artist who made a speciality of drawing museum specimens, or by the influential English ornithological writer John Latham. It shows the wires as much more untidy and straggling.

(*This page*). Twelve-wired Bird of Paradise. Freidrich Specht. Steel engraving from Richard Lydekker's *The Royal Natural History* (1894–96).

(*Facing page*). Adult male and female Twelve-wired Birds of Paradise. Joseph Wolf and Joseph Smit. Hand-coloured lithograph from D. G. Elliot's *Monograph of the Paradiseidae* (1873).

Towards the end of the nineteenth century, William Hart, working for John Gould, interpreted the wires in a different way (*see page 74*). Maybe he thought that their bent crooked shapes were caused by the way the specimen had been packed. At any rate, he shows them six a side, straightened out and neatly folded over the male's back. Joseph Wolf, in Elliot's great folio catalogue of the family, shows them sprouting rather jauntily on either side of the male's body.

J. Wolf & J. Smit, del. et lith.

M & N Hanhart, imp.

SELEUCIDES ALBA

In reality, the wires are not arranged in any of these ways. Friedrich Specht, illustrating Richard Lydekker's *The Royal Natural History*, which was published in 1894, portrayed them more accurately than any of his predecessors. They radiate around the male's tail like unevenly separated spokes of a wheel. But what purpose can they serve? Female birds of paradise are celebrated for their preference for extravagant visual displays by their partners. It is that predilection that has led to the development of fantastic plumes in the males. But how could the female Twelve-Wired regard this jumble of naked quills as spectacular? It must have some other attraction. But what?

Several artists had certainly tried to depict male and female birds together, but none had attempted visually to explain just what the plumes and wires meant, nor how they were used. Then, in the early 1950s, an American artist named Walter Weber (1906–79) produced a revolutionary series of bird of paradise paintings for *National Geographic* magazine. He was the first to show the Twelve-wired male with breast fan erected, but he assumed that the males display in groups, as the Greater bird does. The truth, however, is very different.

The Twelve-wired's favourite habitat is the fringe of pandanus swamps around New Guinea's coasts and rivers. Like nearly all species in the family, the males are promiscuous. Each has his favourite display perch, usually an extremely conspicuous one such as a snag, a bare dead tree trunk standing in a swamp. He flies to it every morning at dawn and then, standing on its summit and slowly turning, he begins to call with a single extremely loud throaty note. If a female is attracted by it, she will land beneath him on the snag. The male, much excited by her arrival, erects his breast fan, and lifts and expands his yellow flank plumes, exposing his naked thighs which are a brilliant pink.

Once this moment has passed, the two begin to dance, sparring with their beaks as they circle the trunk, the male above, the female beneath. Slowly the duo moves downwards. Eventually she decides to retreat no further and takes off, flies upwards and lands on the tip of the snag. The male chases up the trunk towards her, and when the two are once again within pecking distance, they repeat their sparring duet.

They may do this several times until, suddenly, the male swivels round so that he faces upwards and the female is faced with his tail. Then with slow languorous movements, he backs down towards her and brushes her face with his twelve naked wires.

The female Twelve-wired Bird of Paradise has taken a different fancy from her cousins. Her climactic thrill in courtship is not visual. It is tactile.

The Display of the Twelve-wired Bird of Paradise. Walter Weber, c.1950. Oils on board.

3

Cicinnurus

The King and his Cousins
Genus *Cicinnurus*

The Emperor Rudolf's cabinet of curiosities in Prague was a rich one. Alongside the Greater Bird of Paradise, the Lesser, and the Twelve-wired lay another bird skin. The scholars who catalogued the collection also called it a bird of paradise, but it was very different from the others. They were all crow-sized; this one was scarcely bigger than a thrush. They had gauzy flank plumes; it had none. But its plumage was, nonetheless, sensationally beautiful. Above, it was a regal scarlet; below, a silky white with a narrow iridescent green band across its breast. The feathers on its head were so short and soft they looked like velvet. Those on the back glistened like spun glass. Most remarkable of all, it had two long wire-like quills sprouting from its tail. These, however, were not entirely naked like those of the Greater Bird or the Lesser, but barbed at the tip and curled into a tight, button-like spiral of a metallic green that matched the colour of the breast band. It was these spirals that eventually led to the bird being given its scientific name of *Cicinnurus*, a word derived from Greek, meaning a ringlet or a curl of hair.

Judging from early descriptions, this specimen, like many other imported examples, lacked legs. That, no doubt, was why it was called a bird of paradise. Bestowing that name was not a declaration of family relationship, for the idea that groups of similar animals might be biologically related was not one that anyone held in the seventeenth century. Then, each species was believed to have been individually created by God. So the name 'bird of paradise' meant no more than that the birds came from that part of the world, wherever it might be.

(*Above*). King Bird of Paradise (*top*) and Greater Bird of Paradise (*bottom*), painted from
specimens in the collection of the Emperor Rudolf II. Joris or Jacob Hoefnagel, *c.*1600. Gouache
on parchment, 25 cm x 36 cm (10 in x 14 in). National Library of Austria, Vienna.

(*Pages 88 and 89*). *The Ruling Passion* – sometimes called *The Ornithologist* (detail). John Everett
Millais, 1885. Oils on canvas. Kelvin Grove Art Gallery and Museum, Glasgow. For full image
see page 101.

(*Facing page, top*). The crudely drawn illustration that Carolus Clusius included in his book *Exoticorum Libri Decem* (1605).

(*Facing page, bottom*). Birds of Paradise, an engraving by M. Merian. This picture was included in an early edition of J. Jonston's *Historia Naturalis de Avibus* (1657). The illustration of the King Bird is clearly based on Clusius's picture, just as three of the plumed birds are copied from Aldrovandus.

(*Overleaf*). Two early images of male King Birds painted in Java, one showing the dried bird skin with feathers attached, the other showing how the artist thought the bird might have looked in life. Pieter Cornelius de Bevere, *c*.1750. Watercolour on paper, each 50 cm x 35 cm (20 in x 14 in). The Natural History Museum, London.

At the beginning of the seventeenth century, the myth of leglessness took a knock. The Emperor Rudolf II had a Frenchman serving as a naturalist in his court in Prague. His name was Charles Lecluse (1526–1609), though, as was the custom for scholars at the time, he used a Latinised version of his name, Carolus Clusius, in his publications. He knew of paradise bird skins in the emperor's collection and had believed the stories about their celestial origins. But in 1593, he was appointed professor in the newly founded University of Leiden near the northern coast of Holland. There he was one step closer to the source of the paradise bird skins, for they were now being brought back in some numbers on board Dutch merchantmen returning from the East Indies with cargoes of spices. The sailors told him that these skins came from a land east of the Spice Islands that they called *Tanna-Besar*. The words in Malay mean 'Big Land'. This may have referred to the Aru Islands on which the plume trade was focused and which was and is the home of several bird of paradise species. Or, more likely, it referred to New Guinea, the immense island northeast of Aru where the birds existed in even greater variety. And some of these skins that Professor Clusius saw were entire – complete with wings and legs.

So in his book, in which he discusses the natural history of birds, he firmly dismissed the legend that the birds floated in paradise. Nonetheless he repeated other stories about the King Bird. A single one, he said, regularly accompanied flocks of the plumed birds, flying high above them. If a hunter managed to shoot one down with his bow and arrow, then the whole of the flock would 'fall together with him and yield themselves to be taken as refusing to live after they had lost their king.'

He first saw a specimen of the King in Amsterdam in 1603. It belonged to a merchant 'who was wont to buy up such exotic things among the mariners returning home that he might make a great profit from selling them again to others.' Clusius did not buy it, but the following year he saw another one and this he managed to borrow for long enough to have its picture drawn for inclusion in his book. Although nearly all of the other illustrations had already been engraved and were ready for printing, he managed to add this image, since 'no man hitherto (as far as I know) hath set forth the like.' And there the King makes his first public appearance, lying on his back with his extraordinary button-tipped wires dangling – but still legless.

Although Clusius, like his predecessors, grouped the species of paradise birds together because he believed they came from the same place, we now know that birds of paradise are in fact closely related biologically and descended from a common ancestor. The dramatic differences between the males are only skin-deep. The unornamented females, though differing in size, are remarkably similar, just as you might expect from closely related species. They have brown upper-sides and pale lower ones which in many species, including the Twelve-wired and the King, are barred with black.

The displays of the male King Bird remained unknown until well into the twentieth century. His performances not only show off his physical beauty but his skill as a dancer. Each male performs entirely by himself on a specially chosen and regularly used branch. He starts by cupping his wings and fluffing out his scarlet upper breast shield. Then he erects a pair of brown fans which are fringed with the same iridescent green as the breast band. As he becomes more excited, he starts to thrash his wires with their green terminal buttons from side to side. Suddenly he swings over and continues his wire-thrashing while hanging upside down. This continues for a few seconds. Then, closing his wings and glancing from side to side as if he were checking that there is someone around who will approve of his final trick, he swings vigorously from side to side like a pendulum. If there has indeed been a female watching this complex performance and she still remains nearby, he will fly off to her and the pair will copulate.

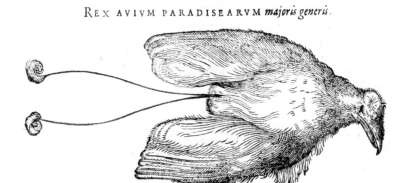

REX AVIVM PARADISEARVM *majoris generis*.

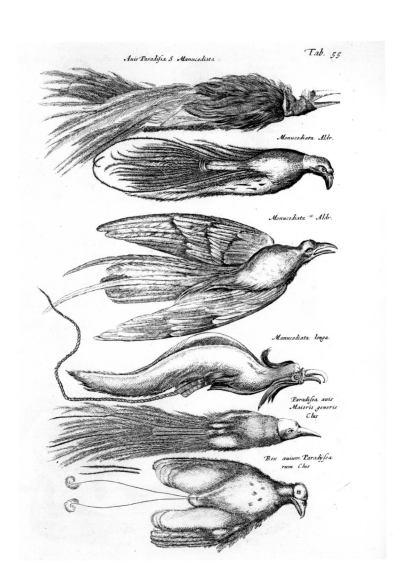

Often, of course, she departs before he gets that chance, but either way he will, with seemingly unquenchable enthusiasm, repeat the whole performance for the benefit of the next female that comes by.

It is not surprising that the Greater Bird, the Lesser, the Twelve-wired and the King were the first of the family to reach Europe, for all are to be found in the coastal regions of New Guinea. No European boats had yet ventured to sail up any of New Guinea's huge rivers where the tribal people were notoriously aggressive and dangerous. So specimens of birds from any distance inland were hard to come by. Nonetheless, some did reach European hands.

In 1771, the French Superintendent of Mauritius, the island in the Indian Ocean then known as Île de France, determined to break the Dutch near-monopoly of the spices by introducing nutmeg plants to his island. So he despatched a number of ships to the Spice Islands to try to collect some. On board one of them went his nephew, Pierre Sonnerat (1748–1814). At the island of Salawati, lying just off the western tip of New Guinea, he met with the same experience as Magellan's men 250 years earlier. The local Rajah presented him with bird of paradise skins.

On his return to France Sonnerat published an account of his travels which he boldly entitled *Voyage à la Nouvelle-Guinée* (1776), in spite of the fact that he had never set foot on the mainland. Nonetheless, he brought back with him a large collection of bird skins. Doubtless, the Rajah and his men were no more fussy about the actual truth of the skins' origins than Magellan's informants had been. If the attribution of a romantic and far distant source improved the price then so much the better. Some skins, for which Sonnerat surely gave a very high price indeed, must have seemed truly extraordinary, for instead of wings they had flippers. They were penguins. These, he assured his readers, came from Papua, as New Guinea was then known. One, judging from the white patch on the back of its head, was a Gentoo, a species that occurs all round the then undiscovered and uninhabited continent of Antarctica and sometimes wanders as far north as New Zealand and Tasmania. That particular skin has now gained immortality. The rules of scientific nomenclature decree that the first name used for a properly described species must have priority over any later one. So the Gentoo penguin, on the basis of the bogus provenance of this one skin, is now known to zoology as *Pygoscelis papua*.

Male King Bird of Paradise.
Jacques Barraband, *c*.1800.
Watercolour on paper,
52 cm x 38 cm (21 in x 15 in).
Private collection.

Barraband

l'Oiseau de Paradis surnommé le magnifique.

Le Manchot de la Nouvelle Guinée.

(*Above*). Two illustrations from Pierre Sonnerat's *Voyage á la Nouvelle-Guinée* (1776).
(*Top*). Male Magnificent Bird of Paradise.
(*Bottom*). The Gentoo Penguin that Sonnerat erroneously believed came from New Guinea.

(*Facing page*). Two male Magnificent Birds of Paradise with a female. William Hart and John Gould. Hand-coloured lithograph from Gould's *Birds of New Guinea* (1875–88).

Sonnerat also described six species of birds of paradise. As well as a reasonably accurate King Bird, he illustrates another, of approximately similar size, which lives further in to the interior of New Guinea. He calls it '*L'oiseau de Paradis surnomme le magnifique*' and accordingly it became known both in English and in French as the Magnificent Bird of Paradise.

At first sight the male seems very different indeed from the King Bird. His chest is emerald green, his back orange and behind his head he has a sulphur-yellow cape. It is true that, like the King, he has two naked quills projecting from his tail, but these lack the King's green terminal buttons and each curls outwards to form a nearly complete circle. In fact males of the species seem so different from anything else that ornithologists invented a new generic name for it – *Diphyllodes*, a Greek word meaning 'double leaf' and presumably referring to the shape outlined by these quills.

The female Magnificent, however, wears a version of the standard female costume and is almost identical to the female King, except for a pale blue stripe behind the eye which the female King lacks. So the latest classification of the family now recognises the affinity between the two species and calls the Magnificent, scientifically, not *Diphyllodes* but *Cicinnurus magnificus*.

There are now not just two but three species recognised in the genus *Cicinnurus*, but although the closeness of relationship between these has only recently been fully appreciated, two feature together in a fascinating painting by one of the nineteenth century's greatest artists.

Sir John Everett Millais (1829–96) began his artistic career as a rebellious Pre-Raphaelite, but ended it as a pillar of the artistic establishment, with a knighthood and the presidency of the Royal Academy of Arts. Somewhere in between these extremes he visited John Gould at his house in London.

Gould was on his deathbed but was so enthused by the visit of the great painter that he couldn't resist showing off some of his most fantastic bird specimens. Perhaps it even gave him the opportunity to look at them himself for the last time. Calling for his daughters (apparently, no-one else was allowed to touch his specimens), he asked them to take some of the most precious birds from their cabinets and bring them to his bedside. Among these treasures were, of course, birds of paradise.

DIPHYLLODES SPECIOSA.

(*Pages 102 and 103*). Three images that Richard Bowdler Sharpe used to justify his belief that the Magnificent Bird could be split into three distinct species. Today, these distinctions are regarded as invalid and only one species (*Cicinnurus magnificus*) is recognised.

(*Page 102*). Watercolour by William Hart, *c.*1890. 59 cm x 30 cm (24 in x 12 in). This is the original painting on which one of the plates in Richard Bowdler Sharpe's *Monograph of the Paradiseidae* (1891–98) is based. Sharpe called this form *Diphyllodes hunsteini*. Private collection.

(*Page 103, centre*). The hand-coloured lithograph by William Hart from R. Bowdler Sharpe's *Monograph of the Paradiseidae* that was produced from the facing watercolour. Hart himself copied his design on to a lithographic stone with a wax pencil and then the colours were added by hand by specialists using Hart's original watercolour (which is now perhaps slightly faded) as a guide.

(*Page 103, top corner*). Hand-coloured lithograph by William Hart from R. Bowdler Sharpe's *Monograph of the Paradiseidae*. Sharpe called this form *Diphyllodes chrysoptera*.

(*Page 103, bottom corner*). Hand-coloured lithograph by William Hart from R. Bowdler Sharpe's *Monograph of the Paradiseidae*. Sharpe called this form *Diphyllodes seleucides*.

So taken was Millais by the scene that after he had left he decided to re-create it. By the time he did so, Gould was dead, so the great painter posed some of his own family members as models for his picture, and scattered across it various bird specimens (a Quetzal, for instance, is shown in the hands of the girl sitting at the left of the painting). Whether or not Gould had actually shown him a *Cicinnurus* species is not known, but there in the painting one lies on the covers of the bed (with just the curls of its tail showing), while the old gentleman playing the part of Gould holds up a stuffed King for close perusal.

In the painting, the careful rendering of the preserved birds may look beautiful, but it can hardly convey the sensational appearance of the living creatures. The male Magnificent's display succeeds in showing off each one of the exquisite features of his unique costume. He displays, not high in trees but close to the ground, and selects a site in which there are a number of young saplings. He snips off any lower leaves that might prevent a clear view and spends many hours every day cleaning the ground beneath, removing every twig and dead leaf, until he has created a patch of bare earth several metres across. This is his court, the stage on which he will perform.

He usually dances there soon after dawn. First he pulses his green breast shield. If a female appears, he may inflate it so much that it becomes heart-shaped and extends up around his neck on either side of his head. If she stays, his excitement mounts and he erects his yellow cape to form a circular fan behind his head. He cocks up his two circular wires so that they stand at right angles to his body. And if he becomes particularly passionate, he opens his beak to expose the lining of his mouth which is a bright enamelled green.

There is some variation in the shape and colour of these adornments between individuals, perhaps giving scope for a female to choose the particular male that delights her the most. Richard Bowdler Sharpe decided that these differences were sufficiently marked for him to define three different species. So he allocated a plate to each of them in his *Monograph of the Paradiseidae*, the last of the great bird books of the nineteenth century. Each is shown in a different posture. But not one of them gives any idea of the way in which the Magnificent male bird actually shows off his costume to his female. Today taxonomists have decided that there is only one species, *Cicinnurus magnificus*.

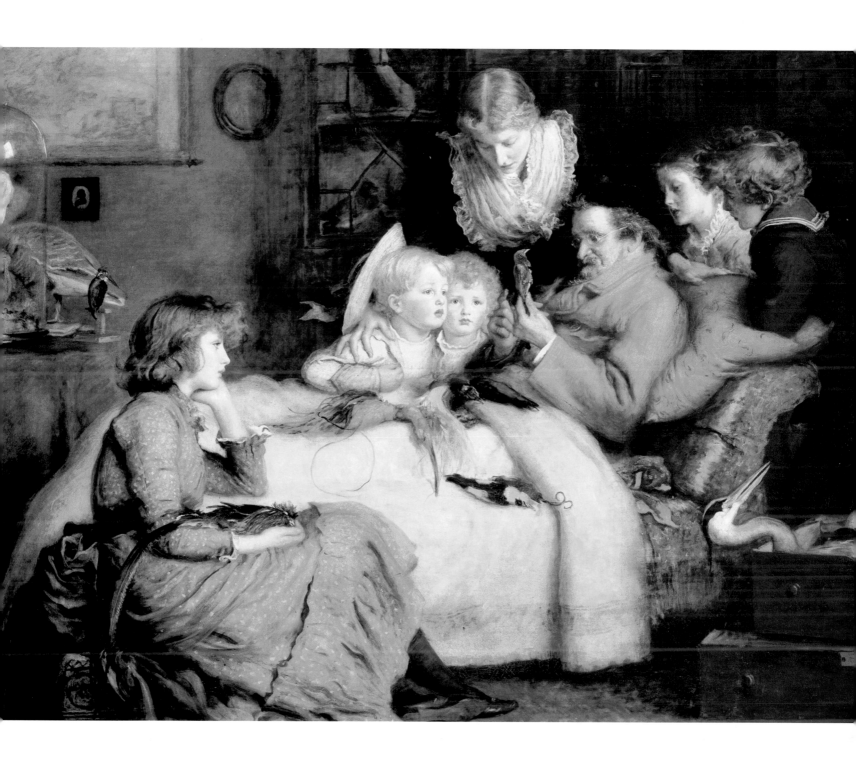

The Ruling Passion (sometimes called *The Ornithologist*). John Everett Millais, 1885. Oils on canvas, 160 cm x 215 cm (63 in x 85 in). Kelvin Grove Art Gallery and Museum, Glasgow.

Although hybridisation is not uncommon among birds of paradise, it is rather strange to find that the King Bird sometimes produces crosses with the Magnificent. This surprise is not because of any distance in their relationship to one another; clearly these are very closely related species. What makes it curious is the very considerable difference in the displays that the two species perform. With the male of one kind dancing in the trees and that of the other on the ground in his own specially prepared court, it might fairly be expected that this would present a bar to inter-specific mating. Perhaps it simply shows the sheer power of the two different displays, and indicates that in the right circumstances they are strong enough to attract females of entirely the wrong sort. The females themselves are so similar in appearance that the males may neither know nor care about any subtle difference!

The hybrids produced might be described as avian jewels with plumage showing clear elements of the feathers of both parents. It would be interesting to know whether they result from the visit of a female King to the ground court of a male Magnificent or whether the cross comes about when a female Magnificent flies upwards to the branch a male King occupies. Unfortunately, there is no answer to this little mystery, and perhaps there never will be. More than 20 specimens – all collected by Papuan hunters – can be counted in the world's museums, but these little hybrids have never been seen alive by ornithologists, and obviously they result from occurrences that are comparatively rare. The first specimens arrived in Europe during the 1870s, and, their hybrid origin not being realised, they were described as representatives of a new species. In accordance with the fashion of the time they were named after one of the crowned heads of Europe, and the monarch chosen as the recipient of the honour was the then King of Holland, William III (1817–90). The Latinisation of his name must be one of the most splendid sounding of all scientific names – *Rhipidornis gulielmi tertii*. It seems almost a shame that because the specimens are hybrids the name no longer has any scientific validity and is now entirely redundant.

There is, nonetheless, one extreme, and this time legitimate, variation on the basic pattern of the King and the Magnificent. On the islands of Waigeo and Batanta, off New Guinea's western end, a *Cicinnurus* species has evolved with a really unusual adornment – an almost featherless scalp coloured light blue. A specimen reached Europe in 1849 and was acquired by an English ornithologist, Edward Wilson (1808–88), who

Rhipidornis gulielmi tertii. A hybrid between the King and the Magnificent. William Hart and John Gould. Hand-coloured lithograph from Gould's *Birds of New Guinea* (1875–88).

A male Lesser Bird of Paradise showing his plumes to a male King. In reality it is extremely unlikely that the two species would have display perches so close to one another. E. F. Skinner. Medium, date, size and whereabouts unknown.

presented it to Philadelphia's Academy of Natural Sciences. There, a description was published by John Cassin (1813–69), who named the bird after Wilson in recognition of his gift. Today it is still usually known as Wilson's Bird of Paradise. But not scientifically. The preserved individual had been seen by Charles Lucien Bonaparte (1803–57), a nephew of the Emperor Napoleon. Grabbing the chance of naming a bird of paradise, he rushed his own description into print, just beating Cassin's in terms of chronology, and thus claiming priority. Despite his grand title of Prince of Canino and Musignano, something of the old revolutionary zeal still burned in Bonaparte's veins. Stating that he cared nothing for any ruler in the world, and directing a sneer at all those who named these exotic species in honour of the royal houses of Europe, he called the new discovery *respublica* – the Republican Bird of Paradise.

Wilson's Bird of Paradise. Carel Brest van Kempen, 2009. Acrylic on board, 15 cm x 22 cm (6 in x 9 in). Bringing the painting of birds of paradise into the age of the internet, the artist released a free stop-frame video showing many stages in the painting of this picture. Courtesy of the artist.

Two images of Wilson's Bird of Paradise, an early one and one that is more recent.

(*Facing page*). Raymond Ching, 1976 (detail). Watercolour, 65 cm x 50 cm (26 in x 20 in). Private collection.

(*This page*). An engraving by J. G. Keulemans from Francis Guillimard's *Cruise of the Marchesa* (1886).

It had taken two and a half centuries, but no longer were birds of the genus *Cicinnurus* the exclusive preserve of Habsburg emperors and their descendants. They had been given to The People.

4

Parotia

The Head-plumed Dancers

Genus *Parotia*

There may seem little visually to connect the birds described in the three previous chapters, but there is one feature they all have in common. It takes a rather different form in each, but it shows a certain similarity nevertheless. It is the development of wire-like quills that emerge from the birds' tail feathers.

Male birds of the genus *Parotia* have no such tail development. Instead they have long bare quills that sprout from the feathers of their heads – six of them, three on each side. In truth these are not quite so wire-like as those shown by their relatives; they are finer and more delicate – and each of the six is tipped by a flag-like ornament of iridescent colour.

Strange in themselves, these head wires become even more wondrous during the display that the males perform. Plume bird displays, and those of the Twelve-wired and the King, may be considered extreme, but they always retain a fantastically beautiful effect. *Parotia* performances are not quite of this kind; to the human mind, they might best be described as ludicrous, a jig devised to substitute for the absence of a clown at a children's party. Beginning with a vigorous shaking of the head that sends the wires into an abstract dance of their own, the bird fans out a hitherto almost invisible skirt of velvet black feathers until it takes on the appearance of a miniature circus tent, or perhaps a crinoline, and then proceeds to hop and run frantically from side to side. At the same time whirling its head around, it twirls and pirouettes like a small demented demon recently landed from another world. But no matter how silly this frenzied performance may seem, it achieves its purpose and the female is mesmerised.

(*Facing page*). Nineteenth-century steel engraving of a male Arfak Six-wired Bird of Paradise, by W. S. Coleman, from J. G. Wood's *Illustrated Natural History* (1872).

(*Pages 110 and 111*). Queen Carola's Six-wired Bird of Paradise, male and immature male (details). Hand-coloured lithographs by William Hart from R. Bowdler Sharpe's *Monograph of the Paradiseidae* (1891–98). For full image *see page 122*.

An imaginative but inaccurate attempt to show two male Arfak Six-wired Birds of Paradise displaying to a female. Walter Weber, c.1950. Oils on board, size and whereabouts unknown.

The first European to see this strange performance was an extraordinary Italian explorer by the name of Luigi Maria D'Albertis (1841–1901). On returning from hair-raising adventures in New Guinea, D'Albertis published a highly entertaining book which, curiously, appeared first in English, even before being released in his native Italy. The book was given a very matter-of-fact title, *New Guinea: What I Did and What I Saw* (1880). In fact D'Albertis did, and saw, many things – some of them now considered quite outrageous – but there is no doubt that he risked his life many times to increase knowledge and understanding of the then virtually unknown island of New Guinea. It was D'Albertis, for instance,

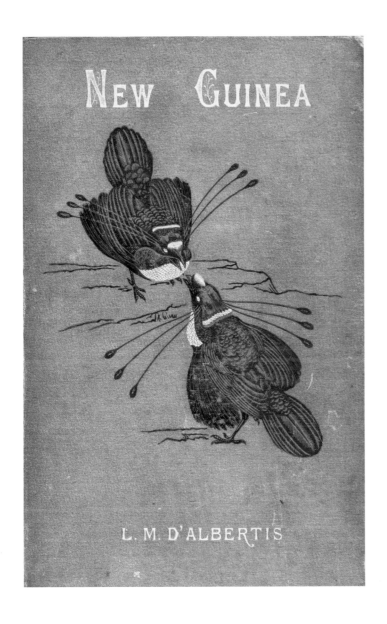

who first obtained specimens of the now very familiar plume species, Count Raggi's Bird of Paradise. In fact it was D'Albertis to whom the rather splendid name is due. Describing his newly acquired specimens, he wrote:

> If this be a new species, as I really believe it is, I purpose calling it *Paradisaea raggiana*, after an old and true friend of mine, the Marquis Raggi of Genoa, a most ardent sportsman and zoologist.

(*Left*). The decorated cloth cover of Luigi D'Albertis' book.

(*Right*). Two male Arfak Six-wired Birds of Paradise. Chromolithograph from D'Albertis' book *New Guinea: What I Did and What I Saw* (1880), after a painting by John Gould and William Hart, dated March 1879.

During one of his excursions into the interior, his native assistant directed his attention to a bird sitting on a branch above a small clearing surrounded by shrubs. D'Albertis had one thought in his mind, and that was to shoot the bird and thereby acquire a fine specimen, but his companion touched his arm and signed him to wait. The bird, at first seeming entirely black in colour, soon descended to its court on the ground and then, in D'Albertis's words:

> He began to move the long feathers of his head… and to raise and lower a small tuft of white feathers above his beak, which shone in the rays of the sun like burnished silver; he also raised and lowered the crest of stiff feathers, almost like scales, and glittering like bits of bright metal, with which his neck was adorned. He spread and contracted the long feathers on his sides, in a way that made him appear now larger and again smaller than his real size, and jumping first on one side, and then on the other, he placed himself proudly in an attitude of combat, as though he imagined himself fighting with an invisible foe. All this time he was uttering a curious note, as though calling on some one to admire his beauty, or perhaps challenging an enemy. The deep silence of the forest was stirred by the echoes of his voice.

The story did not have a happy ending for the bird, and the inevitable finish has the curious ambivalence sometimes shown in the writings of nineteenth century naturalists. For eventually D'Albertis could restrain himself no longer and he did what he originally intended to do. He squeezed the trigger:

> When the smoke cleared… a black object lying in the middle of the glade showed me that I had not missed my mark; and, full of joy, I ran to possess myself of my prey; but as I drew near my courage failed me… full of remorse, I said to myself, 'Man is indeed cruel. The poor creature was full of happiness! One flash from a gun, and all his joy is past… His beauty remains but

what boots it to him. No more than the fame of men avails them after their death… The beautiful creature who, a minute before… seemed to challenge the whole universe to deadly combat… was now stretched inanimate on the field he had selected for his tournament…'. I had not the courage to touch him until he was quite dead.

A nineteenth-century engraving by an anonymous hand showing how European artists imagined birds of paradise (Lesser, Arfak Six-wired and King) might appear in the wild, from *Cassell's Book of Birds* (1875).

D'Albertis' twinge of conscience did not last too long, however. He finishes his account by remarking, 'To show how completely my remorse…disappeared, I may add that I actually ate the flesh of my victim.' Perhaps one shouldn't be too critical; the wilds of New Guinea are not places where a source of nourishment can be disregarded.

This very wildness was, of course, one of the factors behind the order in which the various bird of paradise genera were brought to the attention of European scholars. In fact it was the main one. The arrival of specimens in Europe was very much dependent on the particular nature of the land and the actual habitat that a species occupied. If a species was plentiful and it lived at or near the coast, then it was far more likely to come to attention. If, in addition, it was spectacular in appearance – making it desirable as a trade object – then so much greater was the likelihood.

It was inevitable, therefore, that species living at some distance from the coast would be discovered long after those occupying more accessible areas. This factor applied to an even greater degree with species living only at altitude in the central mountain chain that forms New Guinea's spine. The island's steamy, lowland swamps and forests present formidable problems for the traveller, but the jungle-covered mountain sides that await any who penetrate remoter parts of the highlands are another matter entirely. A person can be just a kilometre or two from the place he wishes to reach, yet cutting a path through the tangled vegetation and endlessly climbing and descending the treacherous slopes might take days.

So it was that the more montane species made their initial appearance on the European stage long after the lowland birds that preceded them. The first of these more remotely situated species to come to notice arrived from an area near the western end of New Guinea known as the Arfak Mountains, and one of these was a Six-wired bird. It is no coincidence that when Luigi D'Albertis observed the display it was in this very range that he made the observation. Yet he was only 50 km (30 miles) or so from the coast for, unlike most of New Guinea's other mountains, the Arfak range descends almost directly to the sea. As far as trade in bird skins was concerned, there was another positive factor. These mountains were close to a small, but long-established, trading post.

For many years this place was known simply as Dorey Harbour, but the name long ago fell into disuse, although the original settlement has grown into one of New Guinea's largest cities, Manokwari. Such changes of name sometimes make research into the history of New Guinea particularly confusing. And the trend continues. The entire western half of the island was historically known as Dutch New Guinea. Then, as it became a province of Indonesia, the name changed to Irian Jaya. Recently another adjustment has taken place and part of Irian Jaya now goes by the name of West Papua. Despite such complications, it can safely be said that it was through Dorey Harbour that many of the first Arfak Mountain discoveries passed, including the early specimens of Six-wired birds.

The frontispiece to a book by Thomas Pennant called *Indian Zoology* (1790). This engraving by Peter Mazell is titled 'The Common Bird of Paradise with a view of Dorey Harbour in New Guinea'.

den Swart Conings Vogeltje

Seventeenth-century watercolour of a trade skin of an Arfak Six-wired Bird of Paradise, attributed to Pieter Witthoos and given the title 'A Black King Bird'. 25 cm x 45 cm (10 in x 18 in). Courtesy of Renaud de Noray.

Quite when the first of these reached Europe is something of a moot point. By the last three decades of the eighteenth century ornithologists had certainly become aware of them, and they are mentioned and figured in several books. This period seems to mark the beginning of the published record, but there is no doubt that at least one Six-wired had arrived in Europe long before this, and there is a picture to prove it. A French enthusiast and specialist in old master pictures by the name of Renaud de Noray has recently discovered a previously overlooked Dutch watercolour from the seventeenth century. It has been tentatively attributed to Pieter Witthoos (1655–92), but whether or not the

Pl. 97.   Pag. 158.

P. Sonnerat Pinx.   C. Baquoy Sculp.

L'oiseau de Paradis à gorge d'orée

attribution is correct, this painting pre-dates anything else known by decades. The fact that yet another new bird of paradise first turned up in Holland is one more example of the influence of the Dutch trading companies and how their pioneering ventures brought back many hitherto unknown wonders from the east.

Until 1885, the only Six-wired species known was the one that inhabited the Arfak Mountains, a species now appropriately named the Arfak Six-wired Bird of Paradise or, scientifically, as *Parotia sefilata*. (The name *Parotia* comes from Greek and means a curl of hair close to the ear, while *sefilata* refers to the fact that there are six of them.) Then,

A Six-wired Bird of Paradise. Engaving from Pierre Sonnerat's *Voyage à la Nouvelle-Guinée* (1776).

(*Above, left*). Male and female Lawes' Six-wired Birds of Paradise. Hand-coloured lithograph by William Hart and John Gould from Gould's *Birds of New Guinea* (1875–88).

(*Above, right*). Queen Carola's Six-wired Bird of Paradise, male and immature male. Hand-coloured lithograph by William Hart from R. Bowdler Sharpe's *Monograph of the Paradiseidae* (1891–98).

as the mountain ranges further from the coasts – those of the Central Chain – began to be explored, another was discovered. D'Albertis had made his observations at the western end of New Guinea, but just a decade or so after his return to Italy, a German explorer named Carl Hunstein (1843–88) was penetrating the Owen Stanley Mountains, a range situated at the other end of the great island. Here he found a species that was very similar in overall appearance to the Arfak birds, but that had several subtle differences.

It was given the name Lawes' Six-wired (*Parotia lawesii*) after the Reverend William George Lawes (1839–1907), a missionary working in southeastern New Guinea. Hunstein made several other important bird of paradise discoveries, including the finding of Prince Rudolf's Blue Bird, but, unlike D'Albertis, he never made it back to his homeland. In 1888 he was drowned in a tsunami that swept the island of New Britain following a volcanic eruption; apparently, he'd gone there in the hope of making further ornithological discoveries.

PAROTIA WAHNESI ♂ & ♀.

H.Grönvold del et lith.

West, Newman imp.

Just six years after Hunstein's death a spectacularly different species was found, and it soon became apparent that it occurred in many parts of the Central Mountain chain. Instead of black body plumage, the male has bright white and golden orange sides. The head is also extravagantly coloured and, curiously, the pattern of this colouration follows – at least partially – a peculiar structure of the head muscles. With this structure, male birds of all the *Parotia* species are able to control the frantic movement of their head wires.

In line with the fashion for naming birds of paradise after crowned heads of Europe, the beautiful new species was named *Parotia carolae* after Carola Vasa (1833–1907), the last queen of Saxony.

But this was not the last of the Six-wired birds. Towards the end of the nineteenth century yet another *Parotia* appeared in Europe. There was only a handful of examples and no-one knew from which part of New Guinea they came. They closely resembled Queen Carola's bird but their bills were marginally smaller and slightly hooked and their cheeks

(*Above, left*). Wahnes' Six-wired Bird of Paradise, male and female. Hand-coloured lithograph by Henrik Gronvold, from *Ibis* (1911).

(*Above, right*). Eastern Six-wired Bird of Paradise. Perhaps a full species, in which case its scientific name would be *Parotia helenae*, or perhaps just a subspecies of *Parotia lawesii*. W. T. Cooper, *c.*1976. Watercolour, 60 cm x 42 cm (24 in x 17 in).

and throats were black rather than buff-coloured. One of these mysterious skins belonged to Count Hans von Berlepsch (1850–1915), a German ornithologist whose collecting drive was such that he eventually amassed 55,000 bird skins. The strange *Parotia* he owned became the type specimen for a new species which, in 1897, was duly named in his honour, *Parotia berlepschi*. But little else was known about the bird. No-one had seen a female – for the plume trade cared nothing for such drabs – and no-one knew exactly where the bird itself lived.

It was not until 1983 that any European saw one alive. In that year, a team of American, Australian and Indonesian ornithologists discovered identical birds in the Foja Mountains, an area of western New Guinea so remote that it had virtually no human inhabitants. The specimens they collected were enough to confirm – at least to some ornithologists – that this bird truly merited its specific status. So now it is known in English as the Foja Six-wired, although, by the rules of nomenclature, science must still refer to it as *Parotia berlepschi*.

And there is yet another Six-wired bird. During the first decade of the twentieth century, another German, Carl Wahnes (1835–1910), despite his advanced years, was exploring New Guinea's mountains and making collections of birds. In a part of northeast New Guinea known as the Huon Peninsula he found a bird that looked rather like Lawes' Six-wired – except for one feature. It had a tail that was twice as long. This was so remarkable that it was immediately accepted as a new species – Wahnes' Parotia, *Parotia wahnesi*.

A comparison of the heads of Queen Carola's Six-wired Bird and its close relative the Foja Six-wired. A drawing made to accompany Otto Kleinschmidt's description of Count Berlepsch's strange new bird of paradise in *Journal für Ornithologie* (1897). On the basis of the differences, Kleinschmidt named a new species and called it *Parotia berlepschi* in the Count's honour.

(*Facing page*). Arfak Six-wired of Paradise. Engraved plate, printed in colours and finished by hand by Jean Baptiste Audebert, from Audebert and Vieillot's *Oiseaux Dorés ou a reflets Metalliques* (1802).

But it is still not certain exactly how many species of *Parotia* there are. In the far southeast of New Guinea lives yet another that resembles the Lawes species except that the little tuft at the base of the beak in front of its nostrils is not white but bronze-coloured. This is enough, some say, for the bird to be given specific status with the name *Parotia helenae*. Taxonomists are not agreed about this, but such variations indicate just how malleable birds of paradise are, in evolutionary terms. The aesthetic tastes of female paradise birds may not change as swiftly as those of fashionable European women, but they are nonetheless still proceeding and seem to be almost as arbitrary.

Le Sifilet. Pl. 6.

5
Lophorina

The Superb Bird
Genus *Lophorina*

I had reached the banks of the Sepik River. There seemed no possible way to get over it. It was broad and turbulent and full of crocodiles. I had my boys build a bamboo raft. When it was done, we put all of my bird of paradise carcases, preserved in salt, on board. I packed everything else I owned: money, guns, binoculars, rolled tobacco, waxed matches, equipment, gear. We shoved off and headed towards the rapids below us, and the flats just beyond that… we went along miraculously for a time… when we ran onto a pinnacle of rocks. The crash split the raft apart. All of us went into the water – my six Kanakas and I – and we were rushed over boiling falls. We landed on the flats – but minus everything. All of it was washed away, birds of paradise, feathers, plumage, salt and all.

Surprisingly, perhaps, this passage comes from *My Wicked, Wicked Ways* (1960), the memoirs of Errol Flynn (1909–59). The great screen swashbuckler had been a real-life adventurer before chancing on Hollywood stardom, and had spent several years drifting around the South Seas in search of fortune. One of his schemes – doomed like the rest to ultimate failure – was to make money from the plume trade. The scheme failed, partly from his own impetuous nature, but mostly because he was too late. As far as the western world was concerned, the trade in plumes was fast drawing to its close. Throughout the nineteenth century it had assumed an importance that is difficult to appreciate today, but more austere fashions were now ruling the day, and glamorous ladies no longer wished to decorate their bodies and clothes with such items.

(*Facing page and* (detail on) *two previous pages*). Male Superb Birds of Paradise with a female. Hand-coloured lithograph by Joseph Wolf and Joseph Smit from D. G. Elliot's *Monograph of the Paradiseidae* (1873).

But before the western world ever became involved, this trade had been flourishing for centuries, perhaps even for thousands of years. It began, presumably, when Papuan tribesmen first realised that the feathers of the beautiful birds they saw in the trees and sometimes killed for food could be fashioned into ornaments. By carefully skinning the bird (instead of just ripping it apart for food), then scraping the skin's inside to remove any lingering scraps of meat, the whole thing would stay intact, feathers and all. If the legs and wings (from which it was difficult to extract the remaining meat) were cut off, the object that remained was relatively immune to insect attack, particularly if the insides were gently smoked. And if moths or other insects did eventually attack – well, a fresh specimen could always be obtained!

Sooner or later a system of exchange and trade sprang up, and plumes from one part of the island were passed along from hand to hand – sometimes for hundreds of kilometres – until they reached a place where the birds they came from were entirely unfamiliar. Small native trading posts sprang up around the coasts, and in time those at the western end of New Guinea were visited by Malayan, Moluccan and Chinese merchants, probably hunting for spices, gold, slaves – anything from which they could make a profit. Now, instead of being taken distances of hundreds of kilometres, the dried skins passed along ancient trade routes and ended up thousands of kilometres from their place of origin. The kings of Nepal wore paradise bird plumes in their coronation hats and the rulers of the Spice Islands gave them as gifts to favoured visitors. And so it was that bird of paradise skins eventually arrived in the western world.

The importance and economic power that the plume trade assumed during the nineteenth century and on into the early years of the twentieth seems particularly peculiar today. Literally millions of suitable birds were slaughtered and exported from their places of origin to the great fashion houses and milliners of London, Paris, Milan or New York. Of course, not all of these were birds of paradise but many of them were, and the trade carried on and on. Particularly high prices were paid for the skins of unusual birds. Best of all would be one that no-one had seen before, and dealers would sort through the bales of feathered skins looking eagerly for such things. And so did collectors interested in the birds from a scientific point of view.

Maria Christina de Bourbon, of the Two Sicilies, Queen of Spain (1806–78), with a hat made from the feathered skin of a Lesser Bird of Paradise. Vincent Lopez Portana, *c.*1830. Oils on canvas, 96 cm x 75 cm (39 in x 30 in). Museo del Prado, Madrid.

The plume birds, naturally, were much sought after, both by
European traders and by New Guinea tribesmen. These native peoples
were also particularly attracted to the long tail feathers of the birds we
now know as Astrapias. A parrot with bright red feathers, Pesquet's Parrot
(*Psittrichas fulgidus*), was in great demand, as were the strange head wires
from the species that the western world calls the King of Saxony's Bird
of Paradise. All of these items still commonly feature in the headdresses
worn by tribesmen for their dances and rituals.

Another great favourite is the triangular fan of feathers – blue in
some lights, turquoise or even green in others – that form a seemingly
metallic breast shield on a small black bird that occurs over much of
New Guinea. This striking fan of feathers, when stolen from the bird
itself, often forms a centre piece to the ceremonial headdresses the
native Papuan peoples wear, and it comes from male individuals of a
species that, because of its intense beauty, is known as the Superb Bird
of Paradise.

The breast shield, so prized by the natives, is not the only
remarkable plumage feature of this species. Adult males have an
adornment on the upper back every bit as spectacular – a great cloak
of long and soft black feathers that can be raised and lowered at will, or
spread like a cape. What the male bird actually does with this cape at the
height of its display is even more amazing. It is spread simultaneously
with the breast shield so that in conjunction the two form a rather ovoid
circle framing what seem to be the bird's eyes. But these aren't actually
the eyes at all. They are two white patches of light refracting from raised
feathers on the forehead, and the eyes themselves peer out from just
beneath them.

Just as the display of the Six-wired birds has an almost other-worldly
effect, so too does the performance of the Superb. Yet this time it has an
almost hypnotic air. The white patches that seem to be eyes stare out with
blind but piercing intensity, almost as if some sinister spell is about to be
cast. And in a sense, of course, it is.

This is a bird of the mountains, but because it is widespread and
common, and also because it was so popular as a trade item with the
native peoples, it came to the attention of the western world earlier than
many other highland species. During the first half of the eighteenth
century, as trade routes to Europe became more established and birds from
the mountains became available to merchants, several hitherto unknown

(*Top*). The male Superb Bird of Paradise in display, imagined by W. S. Coleman. This engraving was produced for the 1872 issue of J. G. Wood's *Illustrated Natural History,* a work that occurs in many editions through the last decades of the nineteenth century. Like other artists before and after him, Coleman was trying to make sense of the bird's extraordinary features.

(*Bottom*). The difficulty of Coleman's task is made clear in this drawing by the Australian artist William Cooper (*c.*1990), which accurately shows the fantastic posture assumed by male birds during display. Like other artists of his time, Coleman never saw the bird in life so he couldn't have imagined it looking like this. Had he produced such a drawing, there is little doubt that he would have been laughed at.

birds of paradise came to light, the Black Sicklebill, the Arfak Astrapia and the Superb, among them. It is difficult to determine which came first. A black bird seemingly referable to the Superb is described in a book on the history of the Dutch East Indies Company called *Oud en Nieuw Oost-Indien* (1724–26). Written by a certain François Valentijn (1666–1727), it contains references to several birds of paradise. The description that probably applies to the Superb is vague and may possibly refer to another species, but what is certain is the fact that specimens became available to European artists within a few decades of Valentijn's writing.

l'Oiseau de Paradis à gorge violette surnommé le Superbe.

La Zephérine superbe.

(*Facing page, clockwise from top left*).

L'oiseau de Paradis à gorge violette surnomme le Superbe. Engraving from Pierre Sonnerat's *Voyage à la Nouvelle-Guinée* (1776).

Oiseau de Paradis de la Nouvelle-Guinée dit le Superbe. Coloured engraving by François Nicolas Martinet from E. L. Daubenton's *Planches Enluminée d'Histoire Naturelle* (1765–81).

Male Superb Bird. Coloured engraving by Jean-Gabriel Prêtre from René Lesson's *Histoire Naturelle des Oiseaux de Paradis et des Epimaques* (1834–35).

Male Superb Bird. A late nineteenth-century engraving by J. G. Keulemans.

(*This page*). Male Superb Bird. John Latham, *c*.1780. Watercolour, 15 cm x 12 cm (6 in x 5 in). The Natural History Museum, London. Latham clearly based this painting on the engraving in Sonnerat's book (*see* facing page) although he slimmed down his subject and left out the tiny bird that had been seized as prey.

These first pictures were wildly inaccurate, however. Among them is one by François Nicolas Martinet (1731–1800). He produced a coloured engraving for *Planches Enluminée d'Histoire Naturelle* (1765–81), a collection of plates assembled by E. L. Daubenton (1716–99) as an accompaniment to the famous *Histoire Naturelle* by George-Louis Leclerc, Comte de Buffon (1707–88). The picture is decorative, rather than informative.

In terms of the actual shape of the bird, the picture given by Pierre Sonnerat (1748–1814) in his book *Voyage à la Nouvelle-Guinée* (1776) is little better, and he makes a fundamental mistake that is extremely misleading. His bird has caught a tiny passerine in its talons, which not only makes the Superb look gigantic, but also implies that it is predatory. The English ornithologist John Latham (1740–1837) noticed this little detail and took it at face value. As late as 1822, in the third tome of his monumental ten-volume ornithological work, *A General History of Birds* (1821–28), he states, 'In Sonnerat's figure a small bird is seen in the claws, from which we may infer that it is a rapacious species.' It is not. It feeds on fruit and insects, and its diet does not include small birds.

Even the great ornithological illustrators of the last half of the nineteenth century had difficulty producing pictures that revealed the bird's spectacular nature and yet remained true to life. The interesting and the dramatic they could manage (as in the lithograph by Wolf – *see page 128* – or the black-and-white engraving by J. G. Keulemans on the facing page), but none of their painted or drawn images is wholly realistic. This is certainly due more to the bird's curiously contradictory features – modest on the one hand, extravagant on the other – than to any inadequacy on the part of the artists.

It wasn't until the last quarter of the twentieth century that the true spirit of the male bird was actually captured. A remarkable series of pencil drawings by the Australian artist William Cooper shows exactly what this bird does, and although the drawings depict the more extreme attitudes that individuals adopt, yet they still remain entirely persuasive images of living creatures.

The Superb certainly has various characteristics in common with some other birds of paradise (black feathers, metallic breast shield, shoulder cape), but there are no species that it can be particularly associated with, and taxonomists place it in a genus by itself.

(*Facing page*). Two male Superb Birds of Paradise with a female. Hand-coloured lithograph by William Hart from R. Bowdler Sharpe's *Monograph of the Paradiseidae* (1891–98).

(*This page*). One of a series of pencil drawings by William Cooper (*c.*1990), showing the postures assumed by male Superb Birds of Paradise during display.

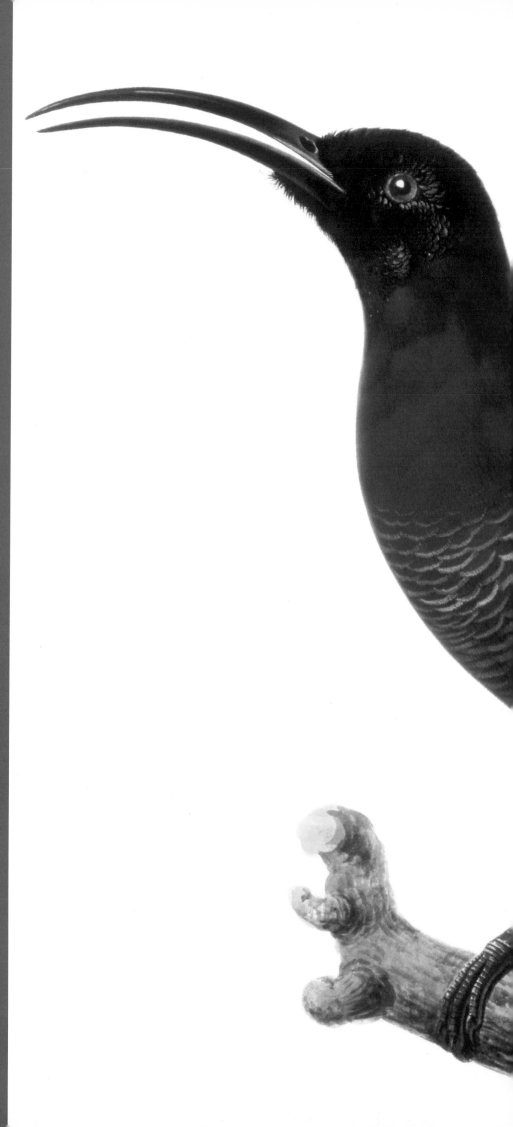

6

Epimachus
&
Drepanornis

The Sicklebills

Genus *Epimachus*
&
Genus *Drepanornis*

If a contest could be arranged to choose the most beautiful of all the birds of paradise – and the various competitors made to display in all their finery – it would prove virtually impossible to select a true champion. There are so many candidates, and each might lay a legitimate claim to the title. Among the plume birds, those with red plumes, yellow plumes, white or blue might all find supporters. The Superb Bird with its immaculate, soft black feathering and iridescent breast shield is an entirely different, but equally deserving, contender; so too is the exquisite King Bird with its breathtaking red, set off by deep green and pristine white feathers. Other entrants can be selected according to taste.

If, however, the criteria for the contest were to be slightly altered, and the competition became one to select the most spectacular species, there could be only one serious candidate – the adult male Black Sicklebill. With its funereal colouring, its great feather fans and axe-shaped plumes tipped by crescents of metallic-seeming colours, it is a fantastic, almost unreal-looking, creature. As well as the features already described, it has a black tail almost a metre (3 ft) long, speckled with iridescent glosses and sheens of blue and green, a back spangled with similar colours, black lace-like plumes at its flanks, and a long, slender, down-curved beak that seems to counterbalance the pointed tail.

(*Facing page*). Two male Black Sicklebills and a female. Hand-coloured lithograph by William Hart and John Gould from Gould's *Birds of New Guinea* (1875–88).

(*Pages 138 and 139*). Immature male Black Sicklebill beginning to acquire full adult plumage (detail). Jacques Barraband, *c*.1802. Watercolour. For full image *see* page 145.

Two stages in the display of the Brown Sicklebill, a very close relative of the Black. Both species perform in a similar manner.

(*Above*). The climax to the display. Pencil drawing by William Cooper (*c.*1990).

(*Facing page*). Approaching the climax. Walter Weber, *c.*1950. Oils on board.

As might be expected, all this ornamental finery serves a purpose, and is put to extravagant use when the bird performs his display.

When William Hart tried to make sense of the peculiar arrangement of fans and tufts, and imagine how they might be used, he came up with two wonderful images, one (*see previous page*) for John Gould's *Birds of New Guinea* (1875–88), and then a second (*see page 25*), just a few years later, for Richard Bowdler Sharpe's *Monograph of the Paradiseidae* (1891–98).

As works of perceptive imagination, and as decorative *tours de force*, they are remarkable, a tribute to the artist's inventive capability. Sitting in England, thousands of kilometres from New Guinea and any living examples, Hart had only imported, preserved skins for reference – dried and lifeless. So strange and eccentric is the arrangement of the ornamental feathers on the Black Sicklebill that Hart was, in reality, confronted by a mass of virtually indecipherable plumes and structures.

From this unpromising resource, he was required to create convincing images showing the bird's beauty to the best possible effect, to breathe some kind of life into the meagre materials that he had to hand, and to depict how the feathers might be used in display. The fact that his interpretation is not strictly correct hardly lessens his achievement. Hart probably believed that the positions and attitudes he created were as extreme as any painter would dare to envisage, but, as with other birds of paradise, the fantastical use to which the birds put their feathers is way beyond any reasonable expectation. It is impossible to imagine it, without actually seeing living birds perform.

At the height of this display the male bird raises his flank feathers above his head like two great sails or sheets, and for a moment looks like a cartoon ghost from a child's nightmare – but black not white. Then he continues to raise them until they meet to form a perfect elipse. Lower down, the plumes and feathers shape themselves in such a way that his head (with a wide-open beak) is framed at the centre of a great iridescent-fringed oval. Meanwhile, the extremely long tail hangs straight down. Sometimes he slowly leans to one side and takes up an almost horizontal position, at the same time holding the oval frame around his head and accompanying the whole with a strange, soft rattle.

Le grand Promerops de la nouvelle Guinée.

(*Above*). Male Black Sicklebill. Engraving from Pierre Sonnerat's *Voyage à la Nouvelle-Guinée* (1776).

(*Facing page*). Immature Black Sicklebill beginning to acquire full adult plumage. Jacques Barraband, *c.*1802. Watercolour, 52 cm x 38 cm (21 in x 15 in). Private collection.

The plumage of the female is arranged in a much more conventional fashion, but even though comparatively modestly attired, she is a subtly marked and beautiful bird.

Black Sicklebills are birds of the mountains and as such they didn't come to the attention of Europeans until well into the eighteenth century. The first mention in western literature is in François Valentijn's *Oud en Nieuw Oost-Indien* (1724–26), but Valentijn's comments are extremely brief, and the species wasn't properly described until considerably later. Eighteenth- and early nineteenth-century naturalists regularly called it a 'promerops', a word they used to indicate various groups of unrelated birds that sported long, slender beaks – bee-eaters, hoopoes and sugar birds among them. The Black Sicklebill seemed to fall loosely into this category, and to account for the discrepancy of its comparatively large size it was often called 'the Great Promerops'. Gradually, however, there was general acceptance that the species was indeed a bird of paradise, and the term promerops is now applied only to the sugarbirds.

Before the end of the eighteenth century the species had been scientifically named *Epimachus fastosus* – *Epimachus* referring to its scimitar-shaped bill, *fastosus* meaning proud – and a fairly comprehensive series of specimens had arrived in Europe. This series included females and immature males, surprising arrivals in view of the fact that it was only the ornately feathered males that were usually collected and traded by Papuan hunters. However this situation came about, there is no doubt that a series of skins was imported into France around the beginning of the nineteenth century, and that at least some of these were skilfully stuffed. The proof lies in several watercolour paintings by Jacques Barraband, who copied the stuffed birds with a delicacy that is breathtaking.

But despite the fact that the species was becoming familiar in Europe via the medium of imported specimens, it would be decades before any European or American could claim to have seen living birds in the wild.

When the mountains of New Guinea did at last begin to be explored by intrepid travellers, there came a surprise. The Black Sicklebill had a close, but quite distinct, relative. Living at even higher

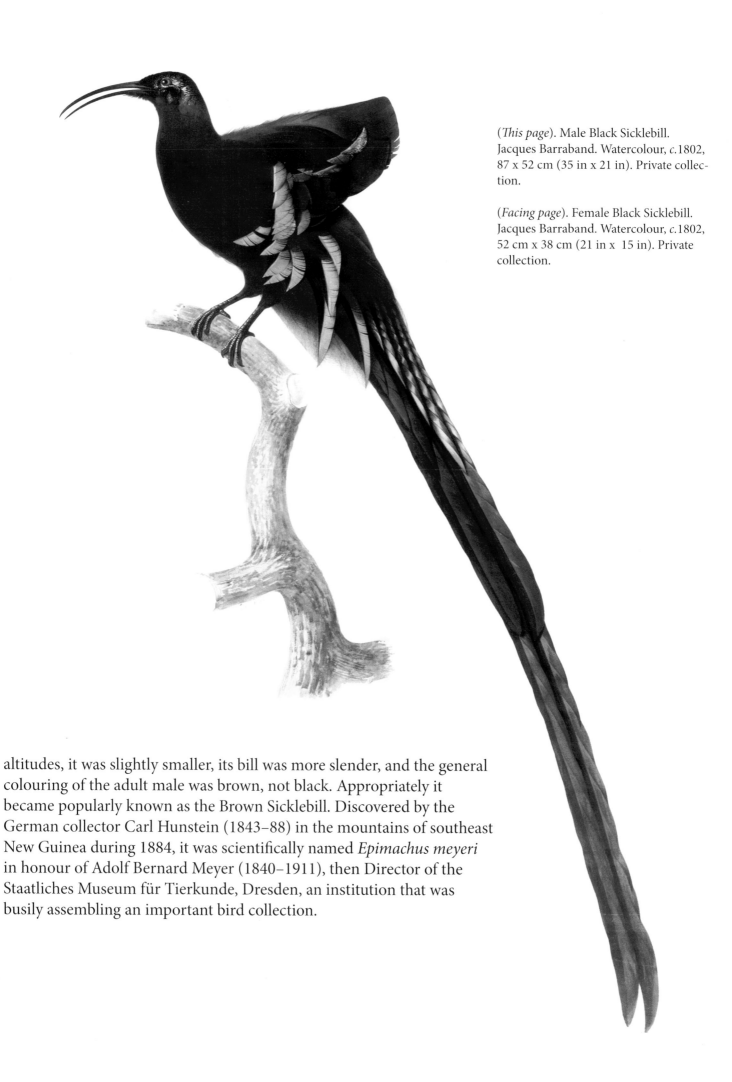

altitudes, it was slightly smaller, its bill was more slender, and the general colouring of the adult male was brown, not black. Appropriately it became popularly known as the Brown Sicklebill. Discovered by the German collector Carl Hunstein (1843–88) in the mountains of southeast New Guinea during 1884, it was scientifically named *Epimachus meyeri* in honour of Adolf Bernard Meyer (1840–1911), then Director of the Staatliches Museum für Tierkunde, Dresden, an institution that was busily assembling an important bird collection.

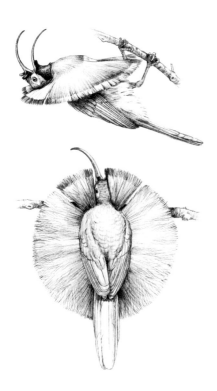

(*This page*). Two display positions of the male Buff-tailed Sicklebill. Pencil drawing by William Cooper (*c*.1990).

(*Facing page*). Male and female Brown Sicklebills. Hand-coloured lithograph by William Hart from R. Bowdler Sharpe's *Monograph of the Paradiseidae* (1891–98).

Later, the species was found to live in many high-altitude localities across mainland New Guinea, and these mountainous areas, which made the bird's domain inaccessible for so many years, still help to preserve it today. Much of the territory it inhabits lies above heights at which land is being turned to agricultural use, and so for the time being the species' future seems secure. The same cannot be said for the Black Sicklebill which – although a mountain species – lives at altitudes increasingly used for farming; it is now one of the most endangered of all birds of paradise.

But these two species aren't the only paradise birds with sickle bills. Just a few years before the Brown Sicklebill's discovery, another species with a long down-curved beak had been found. Although also a mountain dweller with various similarities to its larger relatives, it was sufficiently distinct for ornithologists to put it in a separate genus. The first specimens to reach Europe came from the Arfak Mountains and were sent by the explorer Luigi Maria D'Albertis. The species was named *Drepanornis albertisi* in his honour – *Drepanornis* meaning 'sickle bird', *albertisi* after Signor D'Albertis. Its popular name is the Buff-tailed Sicklebill, and it was eventually found to occupy a very fragmented range across the highlands of New Guinea, being entirely absent in many seemingly suitable areas. In display male birds use some of the devices common to several birds of paradise: they raise their flank plumes to make an almost perfect circle around the head and body, and open their mouths wide. But they also hang in a completely inverted position from their chosen display perch.

Soon after the discovery of this species came another surprise. In the coastal lowlands of the more remote parts of northern New Guinea, there lived a relative, the only Sicklebill that is not a mountain dweller. Named *Drepanornis bruijnii* after a Dutch merchant who first brought the species to attention, it has become known as the Pale-billed Sicklebill; but even today few travellers and naturalists reach its home grounds, and both *Drepanornis* species remain comparatively little known.

There is one more twist in the story of the Sicklebills. A great mystery surrounds a bird known as Elliot's Bird of Paradise. It has come to be regarded as a hybrid but its true nature is uncertain, and although the story starts in 1871, it has no satisfactory ending. In the autumn of that year a strange bird skin was received by a London taxidermist named Edwin Ward among a consignment of exotic bird specimens imported from Singapore.

(*Facing page*). Male and female Pale-billed Sicklebills. W. T. Cooper, c.1976. Watercolour, 60 cm x 47 cm (24 in x 17 in).
(*This page*). Male and female Buff-tailed Sicklebills. Hand-coloured lithograph by William Hart and John Gould from Gould's *Birds of New Guinea* (1875–88).

It was clear that it bore some connection with the only Sicklebill species then known – the Black – but it was smaller in size and showed many plumage differences. The naturalists who saw it were in no doubt. It was a new species that belonged in the same genus as the Black Sicklebill, and it was given the name *Epimachus ellioti* after the American ornithologist and bird of paradise fanatic Daniel Giraud Elliot. The timing of the specimen's arrival was fortuitous. It coincided with the weeks during which Elliot was putting the finishing touches to his *Monograph of the Paradiseidae*, for which Joseph Wolf was providing illustrations with help from his friend and assistant Joseph Smit (1836–1929). At the time of the strange Sicklebill's arrival Wolf had virtually finished all the pictures needed, but there was just enough time remaining for him to produce an illustration of the new bird, and the resulting plate was included in Elliot's book.

Wolf's picture is splendidly decorative but, despite his reputation for accuracy, it is curiously misleading. The satin-like mottling he shows bears little resemblance to the appearance of the actual specimen and it is difficult to understand why Wolf painted in the way he did. Perhaps he simply fell in love with the wonderful image that was developing under his brush and couldn't bring himself to modify it. But the inaccuracy is a fact that has passed virtually without comment, probably because in all the years of the specimen's existence very few people have actually seen it.

The preserved skin passed into the hands of John Gould, and his artist William Hart produced a picture for Gould's *Birds of New Guinea*. This image is more accurate but, perhaps because it is less spectacular, it has been regarded as inferior.

At Gould's death the still unique skin was bequeathed to the Natural History Museum, London. Then, a second specimen turned up. Like the first, it lacked locality data, other than a rumour that it might be from northwest New Guinea. During 1890 it was acquired by the industrious Herr Meyer for his wonderful collection in Dresden. A third anomalous specimen, now in the American Museum of Natural History, New York, was subsequently imported, and this may be an immature individual although it has never been acknowledged to be so.

There the matter rested for almost 40 years. No-one questioned the legitimacy of *Epimachus ellioti* as a species, and it was confidently expected that its home grounds would eventually be discovered in some remote place. As the years passed this possibility receded, and fears were expressed that the species might be extinct.

In 1930 the influential German ornithologist Erwin Stresemann (1889–1972) expressed his belief that the specimens were the result of hybridisation between two familiar species, the Black Sicklebill and the Arfak Astrapia. He lacked conclusive evidence, but such was his reputation that this determination was accepted almost without question. The reputation was certainly well founded, but in this case there are major

Elliot's Bird of Paradise. Hand-coloured lithograph by Joseph Wolf and Joseph Smit from G. D. Elliot's *Monograph of the Paradiseidae* (1873).

flaws in his argument. First, the combination of parents he suggested was one he had already used to account for another anomalous form (known as *Astrapimachus astrapioides*), one that bears convincing marks of both species in its plumage. A second problem with the proposal is that Elliot's Bird of Paradise is a third smaller than either of its supposed parents, and additionally it bears no real marks that might link it to the Arfak Astrapia.

Stresemann's remarks had curious repercussions. Not only was the form dismissed from lists of accepted species and ignored by later researchers, but the original specimen was deemed of such little consequence that experts at the Natural History Museum in London tossed it into a box alongside other apparently worthless specimens with the intention that it should be destroyed. Its survival is down to a stroke of good fortune. No-one at the museum ever got round to carrying the box to the dump! It lay with the trash for many years until a curator by the name of Michael Walters re-located it and saved it for posterity. Whatever its actual status, thanks to Mr Walters this historic relic is now safely under lock and key in the museum's collection of type specimens.

If the form is indeed a hybrid, there is a more likely pairing than the one selected by Stresemann. Affinity with Sicklebills is evident, so the Black might remain under suspicion, but its partner could have been a Long-tailed Paradigalla (*Paradigalla carunculata*), one of the species that lacks ornamental plumage. There is a rather distinctive structure to the tail that is reminiscent of a paradigalla, and there are also small facial wattles that might link it to that species.

And there the matter rests. Elliot's Bird of Paradise may be a species that is now extinct. It may be a bird with a very limited range awaiting rediscovery in some unexplored corner of New Guinea. Or it may be a hybrid. But it is probably not the hybrid that Stresemann believed it to be.

(*Above*). 'Astrapimachus astrapioides', a hybrid between the Black Sicklebill and the Arfak Astrapia that shows clear features of both parents. Hand-coloured lithograph by Henrik Gronvold from *Novitates Zoologicae* (1911).

(*Facing page*). Elliot's Bird of Paradise. Hand-coloured lithograph by William Hart and John Gould from Gould's *Birds of New Guinea* (1875–88).

7

Astrapia

The Highlanders
Genus *Astrapia*

(*Facing page and* (detail on) *two previous pages*). Two male Arfak Astrapias with a female. Hand-coloured lithograph by Joseph Wolf and Joseph Smit from D. G. Elliot's *Monograph of the Paradiseidae* (1873).

The Black and Brown Sicklebills are not the only birds of paradise to have developed extravagantly long tails. Another group also has them. These are the Astrapias, birds whose tails, along with the throats and breasts, have become the main physical focus of evolutionary change. There are five distinct species and each has a tail of breathtaking beauty. Males of three species have tail feathers so long and broad that they make the bodies of the birds look tiny in comparison, an illusion reinforced by the fact that each feather widens gracefully and gradually towards its extremity. With a subtle barring that is unnoticeable unless the feathers are examined closely, the spectacular tails are much sought-after by native Papuans as crowning ornaments for their headdresses. A fourth species has a tail shorter in comparison (although by no means short) that terminates in a flattened, slightly rounded bob, while the fifth species may have the most extraordinary tail of them all. Its two central feathers are the longest of any bird of paradise. White in colour, they are extremely narrow for their entire length, and they end in pointed black tips.

The throats and breasts of all these species are equally striking, and almost unbelievable in their depth and richness of colour. On the living bird the variety and combinations of iridescent and lustrous greens, blues, turquoises, pinks, reds and oranges dazzle as the creature twists and turns in the light. In fact they literally fool the eye, for any pigments that might make up these colours are absent. The colour that the viewer perceives is made up by refraction of light. It is the feather's structure that is the determining factor. At certain angles little or no light is reflected back to the viewer, so the feathers appear black. But as the viewing angle alters, the refracted light creates a whole array of changing iridescent hues and glosses. Birds in the genus *Astrapia* are not the only species in the family that have developed this peculiarity; many show it to similar effect. Nor is it at all uncommon in birds of other families. There are aspects to the structure of feathers that allow the development of this strange phenomenon, and in creatures such as birds of paradise or hummingbirds it is taken to extreme – and spectacular – levels.

The first Astrapia to reach England was brought, surprisingly, by that great panjandrum of eighteenth-century science, Sir Joseph Banks. In September 1770, Captain Cook in his ship *The Endeavour*, after sailing up the eastern coast of Australia, threading his way through the treacherous reefs, shoals and islets of the Great Barrier Reef, turned west and passed through the Torres Straits. New Guinea lay just to the north, but the seas along its southern coast were shallow and muddy and it was impossible to make a full landing. Eventually a few men, led by Cook himself, set out in a pinnace and waded ashore. Among the men was the young wealthy Banks who was travelling as ship's naturalist in some luxury with his own servants. As they walked along the beach Papuans appeared, making hostile gestures and Cook decided to return to the ship. So there is no posibility that his expedition collected any birds of paradise from New Guinea itself, let alone a species that lives in the mountains.

However, *The Endeavour* continued westwards. The ship was now, after two years away, homeward bound and travelling along the route used by traders carrying spices and bird of paradise skins. Eventually it made landfall at the small island of Savu. Here the Dutch East India Company had a representative, a German named Johan Lange, whose job was to safeguard company interests. He and the local rajah received Cook with some mistrust, but there was an initial exchange of gifts, and Cook decided it was politic to present *The Endeavour*'s last live sheep to his host. The rajah then took a great fancy to a greyhound that the self-indulgent Joseph Banks had brought with him, and Banks reluctantly handed it over. Maybe the rajah, in exchange, gave Banks a strange black bird skin that had arrived on the island with some of the more usual bird of paradise specimens. If Banks did not acquire it at that meeting, then he almost certainly did so soon afterwards, for *The Endeavour* stayed on for three days and Banks made a detailed survey of the island.

When at last the expedition reached England, Banks' strange black bird with its iridescent throat was thought so wonderful that the species was named 'the Gorgeted Bird of Paradise'. His original specimen, sadly, is now lost. A year or so later, however, further examples arrived in France. There it became known as '*L'Oiseau de Paradis a Gorge d'Or*'.

Eventually the species was given the slightly more prosaic scientific name, *Astrapia nigra* – the first word meaning 'shining' and the second

Before it was lost, the English ornithologist John Latham drew a crude portrait of Joseph Banks' specimen of a male Arfak Astrapia. Later he used his picture to produce this hand-coloured engraving for his book *A General History of Birds* (1821–1828).

Pl. XLVII.

Gorget Bird of Paradise.

black. Today it is commonly known as the Arfak Astrapia, simply because the species is found only at high altitudes in or near to the Arfak mountains of north west New Guinea. Despite having been discovered more than 200 years ago, the species is still very little known, and such is the apparent rarity of the species that its display has never been observed.

It was more than 100 years before the western world became aware that there was a closely related species. During the year 1884, the German gold prospector Carl Hunstein was working far from the Arfak Mountains. In fact he was operating in the south east, at the opposite end of the great island of New Guinea. Undeterred by grim warnings from friendly Papuans, and accompanied by just a solitary native attendant, Hunstein decided to explore. Climbing high into the jungle-clad mountain ranges, he left civilisation far behind and boldly stepped where no European had gone before. Two years later, in 1886, his German colleagues Otto Finsch and Adolf Bernard Meyer briefly summarised his journey for the English ornithological journal *Ibis*:

> Here the vegetation was sufficient to convince the practised eye that heights had been reached… never before attained… . There appeared a world of new trees and new plants… . The stay in this region, where continuous precipitation renders the preparation of birds very laborious… was an excessively hard task, and one that could only be undertaken by a man of steel and iron… a person of untiring industry and unbroken strength. Avoiding the scattered habitations of the natives, who were by no means friendly, Hunstein passed his time in the bush.

He eventually emerged with three great avian prizes – specimens of three previously unknown (and very spectacular) bird of paradise species. One was the Blue Bird, the second was the Brown Sicklebill, and the third was a new species of *Astrapia*. Naturally, Hunstein sent his specimens back to Germany for scientific description, and his three new birds were named after Germanic dignitaries. The Sicklebill received Meyer's name, but the other two species were given rather more illustrious associations. Currying favour with the crowned heads of Europe being a pastime that was very much in vogue, the opportunity was seized to name these two remaining species after a royal couple. The Blue Bird, as has been mentioned, was named *Paradisaea rudolphi* after

The first illustration of Princess Stephanie's Astrapia (male). Hand-coloured lithograph by Gyulu von Madarasz from *Zeitschrift für die Gesammte Ornithologie* (1885).

Female Arfak Astrapia. Jacques Barraband, c.1802. Watercolour, 52 cm x 38 cm (21 in x 15 in). Private collection.

Rudolf, Crown Prince of Austria, and the third bird was called *Astrapia stephaniae*, after his wife. Sadly, as has been related, the honour didn't bring the couple much luck and the marriage ended in tragedy when the prince committed suicide. Poor Hunstein fared little better. He perished in a tidal wave during 1888 while trying to reach New Britain in a forlorn search for more new birds of paradise.

Just a few years later, yet another *Astrapia* species was discovered, and this one has perhaps the most splendid of all bird of paradise throats. Indeed it was given the Latin name *splendidissima,* which speaks for itself. Commonly known as Rothschild's Splendid Astrapia, it occurs only in the highlands of central New Guinea and was first described by Walter Rothschild (1868–1937), the eccentric English lord and scion of the

Male and female Princess Stephanie's Astrapias. W. T. Cooper, 2005. Acrylic on panel, size unknown. Private collection.

famous banking family. Although he never travelled to New Guinea, it was Rothschild – via a network of agents and adventurous naturalists – who, during the last decades of the nineteenth century and the early twentieth, was instrumental in the discovery of many spectacular species – birdwing butterflies, giant tortoises, and cassowaries, as well as birds of paradise. Eventually he acquired so many specimens that he built his own museum for them at Tring, his family home north of London.

There was now a great burst in the identification of new species as explorers, prospectors, entrepreneurs and even governments looked to New Guinea as a potential source of wealth. Three great colonial powers, Britain, Germany and Holland, carved the island apart in a political sense, although none of them was able to make any real inroads in terms of dominating the land. The bulk export of bird skins brought some small revenue but lone explorers, like Hunstein, who when working in the interior lived largely off the land, were allowed to operate freely. Such people quickly realised that money, or glory, could be gained by finding new or rare species and sending specimens back to museums or private individuals, like Rothschild, in Europe or America.

To the modern mind it seems curious that the collecting was almost exclusively of specimens for museums rather than actual living birds, but there are two very practical reasons for this. First, it was almost impossible to keep captive birds alive in the highly dangerous conditions under which the collectors were operating. Second, birds of paradise are not necessarily easy to sustain when removed from New Guinea. Some success has certainly been had, but too often it is short-lived.

An interesting painting of Rothschild's Splendid Astrapia was produced by Charles R. Knight (1874–1953), the American artist celebrated for evocative and iconic images of dinosaurs and other prehistoric animals. Although these 'prehistoric' pictures were necessarily works of the imagination, Knight's usual method when painting extant creatures was to use a living model. He was regularly notified when an unusual bird or animal arrived at the Bronx Zoo, and would rush off to sketch it, filling in a fanciful background back home in the studio. Perhaps his model for the *Astrapia* was a living bird that survived for a while in New York. Birds of paradise were by no means a speciality of Knight's, so it is difficult otherwise to understand why he would have singled out this rather unusual and little known species as a subject. Certainly, several other bird of paradise species reached New York in the years when Knight was painting.

Rothschild's Splendid Astrapia, male. Charles R. Knight. Oils on panel; size, date and present whereabouts unknown. Courtesy of Rhoda Knight Kalt and Richard Milner. Copyright Rhoda Knight Kalt.

During 1928 Lee Crandall (1887–1969), Curator of Birds for the New York Zoological Society, undertook an expedition to New Guinea with the intention of securing live birds. Perhaps because he was operating at a comparatively late date with better logistics, he was enormously successful. But the success was also due to Crandall's sheer determination and bravery. After leaving Port Moresby, Papua's capital, bound for Australia his ship foundered on a reef. Everyone on board was immediately rescued but Crandall refused to leave without his birds, and these couldn't be saved at the time. He remained for several days aboard the slowly sinking vessel until arrangements could be made for an evacuation that would include all of the precious birds. He eventually reached America in 1929 with no less than 40 live paradise birds, and he made detailed observations of several of them as they displayed, even though they were in captivity. Among these were a Sicklebill and a species known as the Huon Astrapia.

The Huon Peninsula juts out eastwards from the northeast coast of New Guinea and its mountain ranges are somewhat isolated from the island's main mountain chain. Presumably, it is this separation that has led to the evolutionary development of several distinct species there. One is a plume bird, the Emperor of Germany's. There is a Six-wired, Wahnes', that has developed a long tail very much in contrast to its close relatives, which all have comparatively short ones. And there is the Huon Astrapia, a rather plump creature with a broad, blunt-ended tail that is sufficiently different from other birds in the genus to qualify it as a separate species. Not discovered until 1911, it is another of the forms that first came to light as a result of the collecting mania of Lord Rothschild, and his name is commemorated in its scientific title, *Astrapia rothschildi*.

Once again, it is the Australian bird specialist W. T. (Bill) Cooper who has produced a definitive picture of the species. He painted it for his monograph on the family that was published in 1977. To produce this superlative work, he spent some time in New Guinea, observing and sketching the birds in the wild.

There is a significant difference between artworks prepared as informative illustrations and paintings produced primarily for aesthetic reasons. In the latter the artist may paint whatever he sees or feels, and if his talent is great enough, he will be able to express precisely those things that he wants to say about his subject by eliminating or highlighting anything that he wishes. The illustrator, however, paints what he knows to be there, whether he can actually see it or not. He is intent on

(*Facing page*). Huon Astrapia, male and female. W. T. Cooper, *c.*1976. Watercolour, 60 cm x 47 cm (24 in x 17 in).

(*Overleaf*). Two hundred years of *Astrapia* illustration.

(*Page 170, left*). Arfak Astrapia, male. Engraving by W. S. Coleman from J. G. Wood's *Illustrated Natural History* (1876).

(*Page 170, right*). Arfak Astrapia, male. Engraving by Mrs Griffith from George Shaw's *General Zoology* (1809).

(*Page 171*). Study for an illustration of Rothschild's Splendid Astrapia. W. T. Cooper, *c.*1976. Pencil and watercolour, 45 cm x 33 cm (18 in x 13 in). Private collection.

GORGET PARADISE-BIRD.

1808 Sep.r 1 London Publish'd by G. Kearsley Fleet Street.

Astrapia splendidissima ♂

Background

~~Orange fruits~~ (Sk. Book)

for Rothschilds A⁰¹

Podocarpus.

"XAMIGA"

producing a picture of a bird that will include all the details of the creature's plumage. If he knows that his bird should have six white spots on the wing, he will paint six, even if only five are actually visible on his model. His fundamental job is to inform the viewer of the precise 'geography' of his subject. Another artist, pursuing this same subject without the restrictive demands of completeness and precision placed on the illustrator, may choose to paint only what he sees or what he feels about the bird. As he looks at his model, a trick of the light or angle of view may mean that only two of the six white spots are visible and he might, therefore, choose to show only two. In the same idea lies the reason why a hand-drawn illustration may often be more useful than a photograph; the photo will show how its subject appeared at a precise moment in time, but not how it might look at any other.

These differences of approach are made clear if the paintings of Bill Cooper are compared with those of Jacques Barraband. Most of Cooper's pictures are conceived as illustrations for twentieth-century bird books, and they achieve their end with great clarity and sophistication. They provide the reader with all the visual information needed to come to an exact understanding of the plumage of the species before him or her.

Jacques Barraband approached things from a rather different position. He, too, was producing pictorial images that would be the basis for a book, but he was working at a much earlier period, when the requirements of these pictures were by no means so clearly defined. Neither did he know (at this comparatively early period) which characteristics were of critical importance in identifying a particular species. In his eighteenth-century studio, he simply placed a stuffed bird (and there need be no doubt that he was using stuffed birds as models) in a certain light, arranged matters so that all was as decorative as possible, viewed the bird from his chosen angle, and proceeded to paint exactly what he saw. The resulting pictures certainly contain many exquisite details of the subject's plumage patterns, but in terms of a total guide to the bird's features they are not always as complete as we have come to expect from the work of modern-day illustrators. But what Barraband may have neglected to offer us in completeness of plumage detail, he more than makes up for in the truly startling beauty and power of his pictures.

As far as Astrapias are concerned, there is one more species to be described, but it was discovered at a very late stage and so it is included in 'The Final Glories'.

Two paintings of a male Arfak Astrapia, both of which have been subjected to rough handling at some point during their history. Jacques Barraband, c.1802. Watercolours, each 87 cm x 52 cm (35 in x 21 in). Private collection.

8

Ptiloris

The Riflebirds

Genus *Ptiloris*

New Guinea is certainly the headquarters of the birds of paradise, but the three species known as riflebirds all live in Australia. It is true that the largest and most spectacular of them also lives on the other side of the Torres Strait in New Guinea, but the two others are exclusively Australian and don't occur anywhere else. One of these two species, the Paradise Riflebird, has the most southerly distribution of any member of the family; in fact its range lies hundreds of kilometres to the south of any other bird of paradise.

Yet despite this rather unusual geographical range, the riflebirds are in some other respects fairly typical members of the bird of paradise family, for their appearance conforms to one of the standard body patterns. Like Six-wired birds, or the Superb, they are relatively compact in shape. The males have incredibly soft, black plumage glossed and sheened – according to the light – with grape greens, purples and blues, and they have a roughly triangular breast shield of blue or green that appears to the eye to be made of metal.

Their English name is a puzzle. A specimen that arrived at the Edinburgh Museum in 1824 was labelled 'Velvet Bird'. This seems reasonably descriptive, bearing in mind the remarkably soft texture of the body plumage, but other slightly later specimens were called Riflebird. Why, is something of a mystery. François Lesson, travelling on the French ship *La Coquille* which visited Sydney in 1824, stated that it was because the first specimens were shot by a rifleman stationed at Port Macquarie a little farther to the north. Others have suggested that it is because the bird's call resembles the crack of a rifle, though in fact all three species usually produce a double note. Another possible explanation is that some male riflebirds display standing on the top of a tree stump

(Facing page and two previous pages). Male Paradise Riflebird. Raymond Ching, 1976. Watercolour (details), 73 cm x 50 cm (29 in x 20 in). Genesee County Museum, New York.

making themselves very obvious targets for soldiers wanting rifle practice. Yet another suggestion, put forward by an erudite professor of zoology at Cambridge University named Alfred Newton (1829–1907), held that the name probably arose:

> because in colouration [the birds] resembled the well-known uniform of the rifle regiments of the British Army, while in the long and projecting…plumes and short tail a further likeness might be traced to the hanging pelisse and the jacket formerly worn by members of those corps.

Although it might be supposed that the riflebirds from Australia would have been the first to be taken to Europe, this is not the case. The species now known as the Magnificent Riflebird occurs in northern Queensland but also in many parts of New Guinea, and it was birds that were collected in New Guinea that first came to the attention of European scholars. Several trade skins preserved by Papuan natives arrived in London and Paris during the last years of the eighteenth century, and a painting of one of them still exists. The artist is unknown, but the picture is in a portfolio, now in the Natural History Museum in London, that was assembled by the ornithological writer John Latham.

Another specimen – perhaps even the same one – served as a model for one of Jacques Barraband's paintings. An engraving copied from this watercolour was published during the first decade of the nineteenth century, but, surprisingly, it wasn't until 1819 that anyone thought to give the species a scientific name. It is now known as *Ptiloris magnificus*. *Ptiloris* has a curious and perhaps slightly inappropriate meaning – feathered nose. The name *magnificus* is more fitting, for this is certainly the largest and arguably the most magnificent of the riflebirds.

However, its more southerly relative has an equally splendid name, *Ptiloris paradiseus* – the Paradise Riflebird. Similar in overall appearance, it is only slightly more modestly feathered. It occurs in parts of eastern Australia that are now very familiar (from Rockhampton in the north to Newcastle in the south), but it was not described until 1825. Although the eastern coastal regions of Australia began to be settled from 1790 onwards, the hills now known as the Great Dividing Range, just 80 km (50 miles) or so inland, presented an almost impenetrable barrier to the colonists. Attempts to cross or explore it ran into all manner of problems, and those who participated endured great hardships despite being only a

few kilometres from settlements. Much of the land has now been opened up, of course, but the difficulty of the terrain during those early years of settlement is undoubtedly the reason for the comparatively late discovery of the Paradise Riflebird.

It is now one of the better-known birds of paradise and its habits have all been fairly comprehensively studied. Even the nest is well known, which is certainly not the case with many other members of the family. One peculiarity that has been discovered in this regard is that individuals of the species sometimes line their nest with snake skin!

In 1849 John Gould, newly established as a publisher, decided to embark for Australia to collect birds – for the first and last time in his career – as reference for a forthcoming book. In northern Queensland, he discovered a third species of riflebird. Small in size, it is common within the restricted area it inhabits and in most respects is similar to the Paradise Riflebird, which is widespread further south. Gould named it *Ptiloris victoriae*, Queen Victoria's Riflebird,

Two of the earliest paintings of male Magnificent Riflebirds.

(*Above, left*). Jacques Barraband, *c*.1800. Watercolour, 52 cm x 38 cm (21 in x 15 in). Private collection.

(*Above, right*). Anonymous, *c*.1790. Watercolour, 21 cm x 20 cm (8½ in x 8 in). The Natural History Museum, London (The Latham Collection).

(*Facing page*). Magnificent Riflebird, male and female. Hand-coloured lithograph by William Hart from R. Bowdler Sharpe's *Monograph of the Paradiseidae* (1891–98).

(*This page*). Riflebird feathers, plus beak and foot. Coloured engraving by Jean-Gabriel Prêtre from René Lesson's *Histoire Naturelle des Oiseaux de Paradis et des Epimaques* (1834–35).

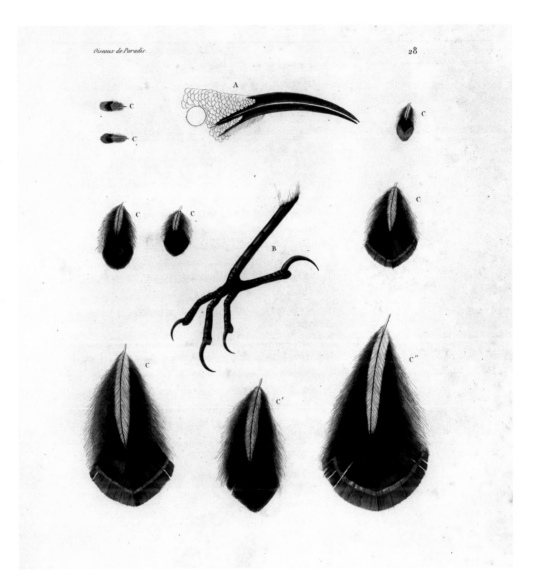

so starting the trend, which subsequently became so widespread among those describing bird of paradise species, for naming their discoveries after royalty.

Riflebird plumage is not obviously spectacular. An ornithological artist, faced with a museum specimen, would not see a need to invent a particularly dramatic display, as some certainly did when trying to divine the display postures of other birds of paradise. A riflebird male has no particularly curious plumes as the males of so many species have, and the flank plumes it does possess are comparatively modest, with its beautiful breast shield conforming to a farly standard formula. So, judging from nineteenth-century illustrations, such as those by Barraband, Gould, Wolf or anyone else, the male riflebird is a

(*Facing page*). Queen Victoria's Riflebird, male and female. Hand-coloured lithograph by William Hart from R. Bowdler Sharpe's *Monograph of the Paradiseidae* (1891–98).

(*This page*). Paradise Riflebird, male and female. W. T. Cooper, *c.*1968. Watercolour, 45 cm x 33 cm (18 in x 13 in). This painting was produced to illustrate Cooper's first book, *A Portfolio of Australian Birds* (1968). Private collection.

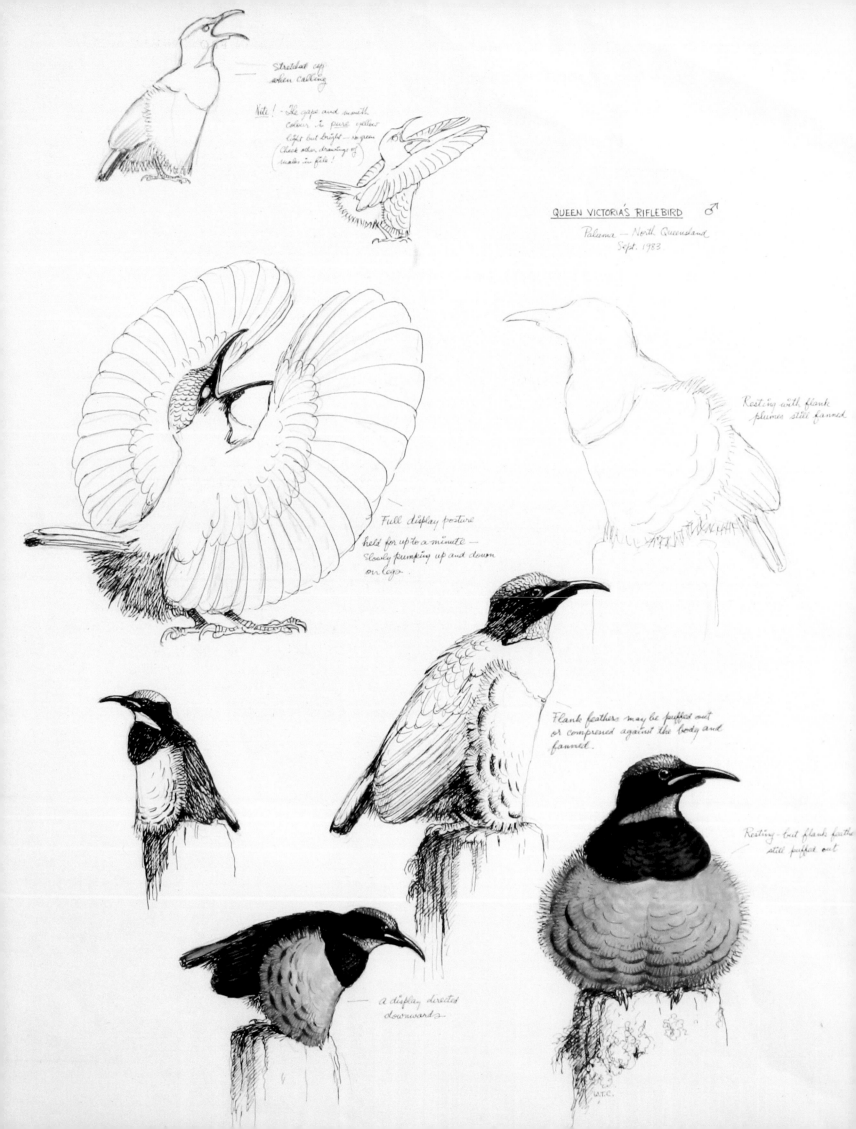

Stretched up when calling

Note! - The gape and mouth colour is pure yellow light but bright - no green (Check other drawings of males in file!)

QUEEN VICTORIA'S RIFLEBIRD ♂

Paluma — North Queensland
Sept. 1983

Full display posture held for up to a minute — Slowly pumping up and down on legs.

Resting with flank plumes still fanned

Flank feathers may be puffed out or compressed against the body and fanned.

Resting - but flank feathers still puffed out

a display directed downwards

W.T.C.

Queen Victoria's Riflebird,
studies of a male in various stages
of display. W. T. Cooper, *c*.1976.
Pencil and watercolour.
52 cm x 38 cm (21 in x 15 in).
Private collection.

conservative and undemonstrative creature. Nothing could be farther
from the truth. He manages to create his spectacular effects with wings
that anatomically appear to have no other function than to fly.

A male Victoria's Riflebird, standing on his stump or on a horizontal
branch higher in the canopy, begins his performance by suddenly jerking
his body erect and opening his beak to expose its brilliant yellow gape.
It is a sure sign that a female is nearby. With an explosive jerk, he opens
his black wings and holds them as wide apart as he can. Slowly, he raises
and lowers himself, bending and straightening his legs like an exercising
athlete. As the female moves around in the nearby vegetation, he swivels
on his perch to keep facing her so that she always sees him at his most
impressive. His wings are now extended and expanded so extremely that
they almost meet over his head and he appears to have transformed
himself into a looming black disc. By now the female may be so intrigued
that she flies towards him and lands beside him on his stump. His ecstasy
mounts and he leans backwards, almost quivering with the muscular
strain involved. Then, if she remains, he lowers one wing, simultaneously
raising the other to its utmost extent and hiding his head behind it. If she
is still there, he begins to alternate the position of his wings, lowering one
and raising the other with such force that the lower hits the upper with an
audible thump. At the same time, he bends his neck from side to side so
that his head remains hidden behind whichever wing is uppermost. The
switching of his wings becomes swifter and swifter. The iridescent band at
the bottom of his chest flashes in the sunlight. The female moves so close
to him that she is embraced by each wing alternately until finally he sways
to one side rather more extremely, closes both his wings, and hops on to
her back. Copulation is then achieved in a brief second.

The riflebirds may not, at first sight, be among the most spectacular
members of the bird of paradise family, but few others can outdo the
males in the athleticism and pumped-up virility of their displays.

9

Semioptera,
Pteridophora
&
Astrapia

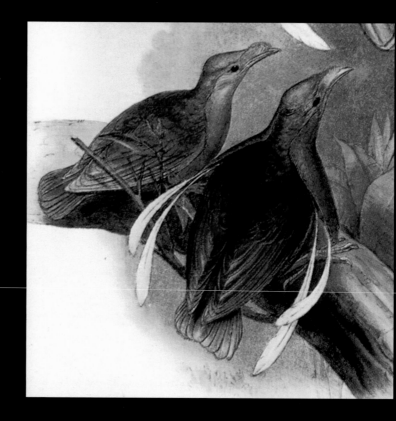

The Final Glories

Genus *Semioptera*, Genus *Pteridophora* & Genus *Astrapia*

(*Facing page*). A painting produced during the 1950s showing how the artist, Victor Evstafieff, imagined that Alfred Russel Wallace might have looked 100 years earlier when collecting birds on the Aru Islands, New Guinea. The birds on the table are two male King Birds of Paradise. Oils on canvas. Down House, Kent.

(*Pages 186 and 187*). Wallace's Standardwing Bird of Paradise, two males and a female (detail). Hand-coloured lithograph by Henry Constantine Richter from John Gould's *Birds of Australia* (1840–69). For full image *see page 195*.

By the middle of the nineteenth century, the bird of paradise family was fairly well known. In Europe, naturalists, poring over the feathered skins in their studies and museums, had identified nearly all the genera. In Indonesia, Alfred Russel Wallace had, for the first time, observed one of the family displaying in the wild and had published a description of the spectacle in London's *Annals and Magazine of Natural History*. But one major discovery was still to come and it was, once again, Wallace who made it.

In October 1858, he left his base in Ternate, a small island in the Moluccas, and set off to investigate Batchian (now spelt Bacan), another island in the archipelago 160 km (100 miles) to the south. He had no certain idea of what he might find there, but he can hardly have hoped to see any birds of paradise since New Guinea, the family's main home, lay 320 km (200 miles) miles away farther east.

When he arrived in Bacan, the Sultan hospitably suggested that he stay in a house in the village reserved for distinguished visitors. Wallace declined the offer. He had now been away from Britain for over four years, living in open-frame thatched huts, and a house with ceilings didn't suit him. As he pointed out in his book, *The Malay Archipelago*,

without access to the rafters he would have nowhere to hang things. Worse still, the Sultan's guesthouse stood in the middle of the village. So Wallace asked for, and was given, a simple hut on the edge of the forest.

The day after he arrived, he and his Malay assistant, Ali, set out to make a preliminary survey, Ali going one way, Wallace another. When they met that evening on their return, Ali showed him what he had collected. Wallace was astounded and wrote:

'I saw a bird with a mass of splendid green feathers on its breast, elongated into two glittering tufts; but, what I could

not understand, was a pair of long white feathers which stuck straight out from each shoulder. Ali assured me that the bird stuck them out this way itself when fluttering its wings and said that they had remained so without his touching them. I now saw that I had got a great prize, no less than a completely new form of the Bird of Paradise, differing most remarkably from every other known bird.'

It was about the size of a jay. Its huge triangular breast shield of iridescent green was certainly beautiful, but the two white feathers projecting from each wing were truly extraordinary. Wallace called them 'standards' since that term was already used by ornithologists for a pair of disproportionately long feathers, one on each wing, carried by a species of African nightjar. But these were significantly different, for whereas the nightjar's standards trailed behind the bird in flight, those of this new bird of paradise were each separately muscled, as Wallace discovered when he dissected one of the specimens. He knew, therefore, that the bird was capable of moving them independently, just as Ali had said.

After this discovery, he continued on to the neighbouring and larger island of Halmahera and there he found another population of this extraordinary bird.

Thrilled by these discoveries, on 29 October 1858, he wrote an excited letter, replete with underlinings and exclamation marks, to Samuel Stevens (1817–99) his agent in London. "I have already the finest and most wonderful bird in the island. I have a good mind to keep it a secret but I cannot resist telling you. I have a new bird of paradise! of a new genus!! quite unlike anything yet known, very curious and handsome!!!"

Stevens sent this letter, together with Wallace's rough sketch of the bird, to the Zoological Society of London, and in March 1859 it was read out at the Society's meeting. George Gray (1808–72), the British Museum ornithologist, supplied a written note proposing that this wonderful bird should be named, in honour of its discoverer, *Paradisaea wallacei*.

By June, Wallace's specimens themselves had reached London and were duly displayed at the next meeting of the Zoological Society by John Gould, who was by now a well-respected avian taxonomist. He suggested that they were so extraordinary they should be given a

Male Wallace Standardwing. Walter Weber, *c.*1950. Oils on board, size unknown. The caption for the magazine article which this painting once accompanied reads, 'A Bird to Make you Rub your Eyes'.

(*This page*). A page from the notebook in which Wallace listed the specimens he collected while at Batchian (Bacan) in 1858. A later hand, that of G. R. Gray, then in charge of the bird collection in the British Museum, has inserted the newly coined Latin name for the Standardwing, *Semioptera wallacei*, and initialled his addition. This notebook is in the collection of the Natural History Museum, London.

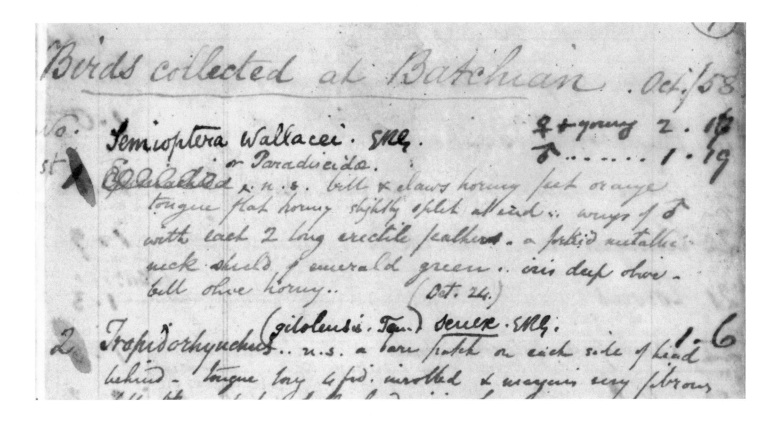

genus of their own and proposed that *Paradisaea* in their name should be changed to *Semioptera*, a word derived from the Greek meaning roughly 'standardwing'.

(*Above*). Detail from the same page showing the section that lists the Standardwing.

Then he went further. He questioned whether the bird was really a bird of paradise at all. Perhaps, he suggested, it was allied to the riflebirds which, conveniently for Gould and the publication he was working on, lived in Australia as well as New Guinea.

Gould was eager to publish the discovery as soon as possible. He had just released the first two parts of a *Supplement* to his *Birds of Australia*. So the following September, in spite of the fact that the Standardwing lived several hundred kilometres away from the continent in the supplement's title, a plate of the bird duly appeared in the third part. It was drawn by Henry Constantine Richter (1821–1902), an accomplished ornithological illustrator who was one of Gould's regular artists.

Judging from the plate, neither Richter nor Gould, who normally supplied rough layouts of the plates he commissioned, truly believed that the birds could erect their extraordinary standards, for although Gould regularly

showed birds in what he supposed to be their display postures, the Standardwing's white wing plumes are shown hanging somewhat limply by the bird's side. Even John Gerrard Keulemans (1842–1912), when he supplied the illustration of the bird for Wallace's own book in 1869, shows the most prominent individual with its standards at what might be described as half-cock.

The species' island homes, Bacan and Halmahera, remained little explored by Europeans until well into the twentieth century, and for some time ornithologists were uncertain as to whether the species

(*This page, above*). Wallace's Standardwing Bird of Paradise, two males and a female. Hand-coloured lithograph by William Hart from R. Bowdler Sharpe's *Monograph of the Paradiseidae* (1891–98).

(*This page, right*). Wallace's Standardwing Bird of Paradise, male and female. John Gould, *c.*1860. Watercolour, 15 cm x 13 cm (6 in x 5 in). This rudimentary unsigned watercolour has a Gould family provenance. It seems to be a provisional layout for the two upper birds in the lithograph shown above (which, interestingly, was not published until some years after Gould's death). The image of the male may in turn be partly based on one of the lower birds in an earlier Gould-inspired picture (shown opposite). Private collection.

(*Facing page*). Wallace's Standardwing Bird of Paradise, two males and a female. Hand-coloured lithograph by Henry Constantine Richter from John Gould's *Birds of Australia* (1840–69).

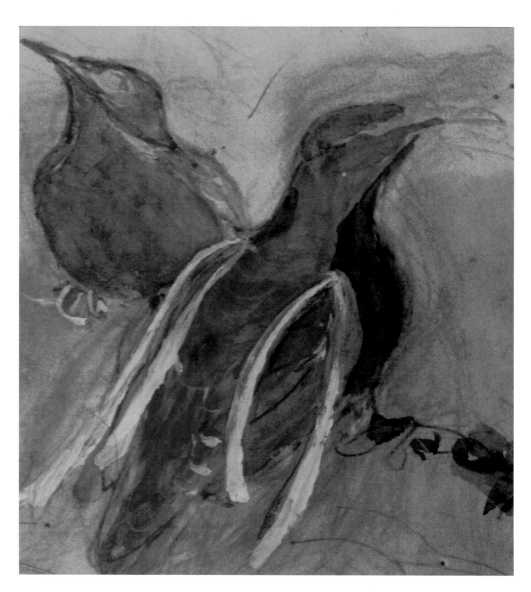

SEMIOPTERA WALLACEII, *Gray*

J. Gould and H.C. Richter, del. et lith.   Hullmandel & Walton Imp.

still survived. But in 1927, a British animal collector, Walter Goodfellow (1866–1953), not only rediscovered the bird on Halmahera, but wrote a full description of its display.

The birds assemble early in the morning, in the tops of low trees in groups of at least thirty or forty. As dawn breaks they start a more or less constant chatter of calls among themselves while excitedly fluttering back and forth, erecting their green cravats, beating their wings and sometimes, as the calls mount to a crescendo, swivelling on a branch to hang upside down beneath it.

But the males also have another display trick all of their own that has only recently been described. While singing excitedly, one will suddenly leap vertically upwards. Flapping vigorously, he rises for 6 metres (20 ft) or so in the air and then suddenly stops beating his wings and, holding them outstretched, floats downwards headfirst, so that the rush of air makes his white standards vibrate and become a white blur alongside each wing until eventually he lands on the perch from which he took off – or very close by.

This extraordinary display is not the only thing that sets the Standardwing apart from other birds of paradise. It is also one of only two species living in the Moluccas (the Paradise Crow, a species in which males and females are similar, is the other), an archipelago far beyond the recognised zoological limits of the family headquarters in New Guinea, and its offshore islands.

Is it truly a member of the Paradiseidae? Or was Wallace led to categorise it as such by his own enthusiasm for the family? Gould's suggestion that it might be related to riflebirds seems not very revolutionary today, for now riflebirds themselves have been recognised as members of the Paradiseidae.

Later suggestions have been more radical. Some ornithologists have pointed out that were it not for its standards and emerald breast shield, the Standardwing would look very like a friarbird, a group that has members not only all over New Guinea but in most parts of Australia. It has much the same sharp down-curved somewhat aggressive-looking beak. Perhaps DNA will eventually reveal the correct taxonomic placing of the bird, but meanwhile it remains a bird of paradise. It would be a pity indeed to remove the species that bears Wallace's name from the group that he loved the most.

Wallace's Standardwing Bird of Paradise, two males and a female. Engraving by John Gerrard Keulemans from A. R. Wallace's *The Malay Archipelago* (1869).

In the decades that followed, more species of the long-established genera were found – more Six-wireds, more Sicklebills, even more birds of the classic plumed kind. Goldie's Bird (*Paradisaea decora*), which has plumes of a rather richer red than those of Count Raggi's bird, was discovered in 1883 on tiny islands off the eastern tip of the main island, then part of the British Empire, and five years later another variant was found on the Huon Peninsula, with plumes that, though yellow at the base, are for most of their length a gauzy white. That part of New Guinea was at the time claimed by Germany, and in consequence it was named the Emperor of Germany's Bird (*Paradisaea guilielmi*).

Then in 1894 came a sensation – a species that looked rather like the Stitchbird of New Zealand. But it had a kind of decoration not only unlike that of any other bird of paradise but one unparalleled in the whole of the world of birds. Adolf Bernard Meyer (1840–1911), the Director of the Dresden Museum who was instrumental in the discovery of many birds of paradise, first described the species from a specimen collected in the still largely unexplored mountain ranges of central New Guinea. Meyer loyally named it *Pteridophora alberti* after his king. In English it is known as the King of Saxony's Bird of Paradise.

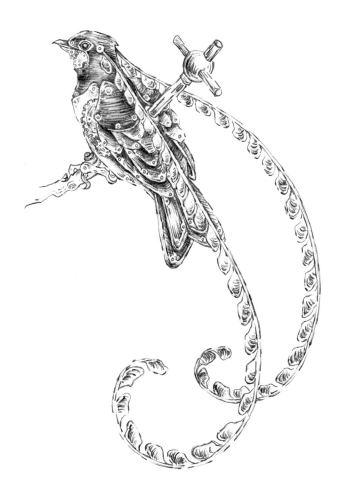

(*Above*). A fanciful interpretation of a male King of Saxony's Bird of Paradise by Greek artist Vaso Kafkoula, from a series of bird illustrations called 'Clockwork Creatures'. Mixed media, *c*.2009. By kind permission of the artist and vasodelirium.blogspot.com

It is about the same size as a Six-wired bird and the female looks not unlike a female of that genus. But the male is astoundingly different. Two extraordinary decorations sprout from the back of his neck. Though they are clearly feathers, it would be hard to recognise them as such if they were found unattached to a bird. They are over three times as long as his body. The quill lacks any barbs of the normal kind. One side, in fact, is totally bare. The other carries a line of thirty to forty rectangular platelets like tiny flags. Their underside is a dull grey, but above they are a wonderful pearly blue with a surface more like that of a shell than a feather. So stunningly distinctive are these ornaments that Papuans regularly use them to decorate their headdresses.

A displaying male exploits these remarkable ornaments to the full. He starts by singing a strange hissing song high up on the forest canopy.

Then he comes down to his regular display perch – the bottom curve of a looped hanging liana. Still hissing and squeaking, he flexes his legs repeatedly and vigorously. Soon he is bouncing up and down on his springy vine with all the determined enthusiasm of a child on a playground swing. By this time, a female may have arrived and she perches a little above him on the vine. She too appears to be enjoying the ride. To begin with he holds his head plumes as he normally does, pointing horizontally over his back and extending far beyond his tail so that as he bounces they sway gracefully along their length. But soon he begins to move them, each independently, if he so wishes. Sometimes he holds them at right angles to his head. Sometimes he swings one vertically upwards while holding the other vertically downwards. The female stays on the vine a short distance above him, until, with plumes a-swirling, he hops with increasing speed up the vertical vine and the pair copulate.

The discovery of this almost unbelievable bird came at the very end of the nineteenth century, and it might have seemed, as the twentieth century dawned, that the bird of paradise family had now been fully revealed. But there was just one more glory to come.

It took some time to appear. After the Great War of 1914–18, Germany lost control of its territory in the island, and Australia, which had taken over British responsibilities, administered all the eastern half. Much of the interior was still unexplored.

In 1935, a young and extremely tough patrol officer, Jack Hides (1906–38), set off to explore the unknown mountains between the Strickland and Purari rivers. He took with him an Irish-Australian assistant, ten armed New Guinea policemen, and 28 locally recruited carriers. It was the last major exploring expedition in Australian New Guinea that had no radio or aerial support, and it lasted six months. They took steel axe-heads with them to use in bartering for food, but the people they encountered, who had never seen Europeans

The first illustration of the male Ribbon-tail Bird of Paradise, with and without its long tail feathers. Lilian Medland. Watercolour reproduced in *The Australian Zoologist* (1939). Whereabouts and size of original unknown.

before, were not interested in such things. They preferred their stone axes. There were fights and ambushes. Lives were lost on both sides. Halfway through, after making camp at an altitude of 2,250 m (7,500 ft), Hides climbed a tree to try and see what lay ahead, and work out the best route between the mountain peaks confronting him. Later, he wrote:

> as I stood in the branches gazing at the rock- and
> heather-covered summit of the peaks in front of us,
> I noticed pairs of an interesting species of paradise
> birds flitting through the moss-covered branches of
> the trees ahead of me. The males had two ivory-white
> feathers as a tail with which they made flicking noises
> as they trailed the plumes after them through the air.
> I did not know of this species so for the information
> of our ornithological department, I instructed one of
> the police to shoot a male bird, remove the tail feathers
> and carefully pack them away.

Exactly what happened to those feathers subsequently is a mystery, but the fact that a possibly unknown species had been discovered came to the notice of Fred Shaw Mayer (1899–1989), a young bird collector working in the island. He started to search for the birds, but although he failed to find a living specimen he did secure a pair of long white feathers that must have belonged to the mystery bird. They had been collected by a missionary who had noticed them in the headdress worn by one of the tribesmen in the Wahgi, the wide valley that runs east to west like a long crease through the central mountain ranges. Shaw Mayer sent them to London where they were examined by one of the ornithologists at the British Museum, Charles Stonor (1912–82). He concluded that they did indeed come from a hitherto unknown species and promptly – perhaps even a little precipitously, since they were the only material evidence he had – published a description of them, attributing them to a new species of *Astrapia* which he called *mayeri*. It was also given an English name – the Ribbon-tailed Bird of Paradise.

Meanwhile, another Australian patrol was exploring the mountains between the central Wahgi valley and the Sepik River which drains northeastern New Guinea. At high altitudes they too saw a bird with extremely long white tail plumes, and they collected, not just the tail feathers, but complete specimens which were sent to the Australian Museum in

Sydney. Unaware of what was happening in London, the Australian taxonomists also described their bird, and not only gave it a specific name but allocated it to a new genus, *Taeniaparadisaea macnicolli*. However, since the rules of scientific nomenclature dictate that the first name given is the one that survives, Fred Shaw Mayer, who was one of the most modest and retiring of men, still retains his celebrity.

The Ribbon-tail has one of the most limited distributions of all the mainland species. It occurs only in the high moss forest at altitudes of 3,000–3,300 m (10,000–11, 000 ft) on the peaks around Mount Hagen in the very heart of the New Guinea highlands. The sheer length of its great white tail makes it very conspicuous and also prevents it from indulging in complicated gymnastic displays. To attract a mate, the male simply flies back and forth between two relatively close perches, landing each time with a thump and then thrashing its immense tail like an angry cat.

By the time the Ribbon-tail was discovered, Richard Bowdler Sharpe's celebrated monograph on the family had long since been printed. But the species appears in its full splendour in the 1977 monograph illustrated by William Cooper. In Cooper's picture a pair of birds are perched on the substantial branch of what is clearly an emergent tree – the male with his long tail catching slightly awkwardly on the bough – feeding on the small fruits that Cooper had actually seen them eating.

For the first time since Aldrovandus portrayed a legless bird of paradise floating in heaven, four hundred years earlier, the birds were shown to the world by an artist who had seen them alive in the wild.

(*Previous two pages*). Ribbon-tail Bird of Paradise, male. Errol Fuller, 1993. Oils on panel, 19 cm x 39 cm (7 ½ in x 15 ½ in). Private collection.

(*Facing page*). Ribbon-tail Bird of Paradise, male and female. W. T. Cooper, *c*.1976. Watercolour, 60 cm x 47 cm (24 in x 17 in).

W.T. Cooper. '74.

10

The Meaning of the Dances

208

The Eggs of some Birds of Paradise, together with the eggs of a few Bower Birds. There is considerable similarity between the eggs of certain species, yet sometimes a surprising variation between individual eggs of birds belonging to the same species. Chromolithograph by Henrik Gronvold from *Novitates Zoologicae* (1910).

(*Top row, from left*). Count Raggi's Bird of Paradise; Twelve-wired Bird of Paradise; Count Raggi's Bird of Paradise; Prince Rudolf's Blue Bird of Paradise; Queen Victoria's Riflebird.

(*Second row, from left*). Lesser Bird of Paradise; Lesser Bird of Paradise; Princess Stephanie's Astrapia; Magnificent Riflebird; Trumpet Bird.

(*Third row, from left*). Curl-crested Manucode; Glossy-mantled Manucode; Crinkle-collared Manucode; White-eared Catbird.

(*Fourth row, from left*). Great Bower Bird; Great Bower Bird; Fawn-breasted Bower Bird; Tooth-billed Bower Bird.

(*Fifth row, from left*). Black-eared Catbird; Lawes' Six-wired Bird of Paradise; Newton's Bower Bird; Superb Bird of Paradise; Superb Bird of Paradise.

H.Gronvold pinx.

C.Hodges & Son,lith.

EGGS OF PARADISEIDAE.

The Meaning of
the Dances

Alfred Wallace was not at all sure why male birds of paradise had such extravagant plumes. On the face of it, they contradicted his theory of evolution by natural selection drafted four years after his arrival in Indonesia and subsequently read out to a meeting of the Linnean Society in London during 1858. The theory had been summarised as 'the survival of the fittest'. But how could huge plumes that made a bird extremely conspicuous, that in some instances impeded it in flight and that in all cases clearly made great demands on an individual's physical resources to grow – how could such things aid a bird's survival?

Wallace recognised, of course, that a bird's plumage may carry colours and patterns because, as he put it, 'one of the first needs of a new species would be to keep separate from its nearest allies and that this could be done by some easily seen marks of difference'. Female birds of paradise, however, like the females of many other species, are plain and drab and lack the male's extravagant colours. Why should that be? Wallace suggested that it was because such bright plumage would make a female, sitting on her nest, very conspicuous and therefore very vulnerable to predators. In support of that explanation, he pointed out that many birds in which both sexes are brightly coloured – such as kingfishers and trogons – make their nests in tunnels where the female's bright colours are invisible and therefore no liability. But even he must have recognised that plumes of a bird of paradise were considerably more spectacular than is necessary simply to identify species.

Charles Darwin, whose paper on natural selection had been read out at the same historic Linnean meeting, also saw the difficulty. He, however, proposed a fundamentally different explanation, a process that has little to do with the survival of the fittest. He called it 'sexual selection',

(*Above*). An early attempt to show a plume bird of paradise in display. Anonymous, *c.*1820. Watercolour, 48 cm x 60 cm (19 in x 24 in). This is one of a series of paintings of birds (now in the Natural History Museum, London) commissioned in Canton by John Reeves, an English resident.

(*Pages 206 and 207*). Count Raggi's and Lesser Birds of Paradise, males and females. Details from two paintings by W. T. Cooper. Both oils on canvas, *c.*2000. Private collection. For full images *see page 210*.

Count Raggi's Bird of Paradise, two males displaying to a female. W. T. Cooper, *c*.2000. Oils on canvas, 90 cm x 125 cm (35 in x 52 in). Private collection.

and he explained it in an even longer book than *On The Origin of Species,* a book which he entitled *The Descent of Man and Selection in Relation to Sex.* According to this explanation, male birds of paradise display their plumes to females who then – having surveyed all available candidates – choose the one that most appeals to them visually.

Wallace would have none of it. In reviewing *The Descent of Man* he wrote, 'Are we to believe that the actions of an ever varying fancy for a slight change of colour could produce and fix the definite colours and markings which actually characterise species?' Furthermore, he said, it was unacceptable to suggest that birds had an aesthetic sense. That would be crediting a bird with a human characteristic for which there was no evidence. It would be anthropomorphism at its most unjustified.

Darwin emphatically rebutted the charge. 'Birds,' he wrote, 'are the most aesthetic of all animals, excepting of course man, and they have the same taste for the beautiful as we have.' He was writing in this particular instance about bird song, but the statement applied even more obviously and spectacularly to the plumage of birds of paradise. That he was right has been proved subsequently by a whole range of experiments. Ornithologists have both snipped off and added to the 'eyes' on a peacock's wonderful tail-train and shown that peahens will always select the male with the greater number. A similar thing is true for African why-dah birds. Here the males, during the breeding season, develop long glossy black tail feathers which they show off to visiting females. Trim a successful male's tail and he will be spurned. Add to it, and a bird that

Lesser Bird of Paradise, two males displaying to a female. W. T. Cooper, c.2000. Oils on canvas, 90 cm x 125 cm (35 in x 52 in). Private collection.

had only produced a medium-sized tail would suddenly become – no doubt to his considerable gratification – suddenly favoured. The same, doubtless, would be true for birds of paradise, though seemingly no-one has been unfeeling enough to inflict such barbarity on one of them.

Greater Birds, the species that Wallace first observed in display, gather together for these competitions, usually in a tall tree with relatively open upper branches where the birds can be easily seen as a group. There may be as many as twenty or so and they occupy their display tree for most of the year though their numbers are usually highest between December and February. The arrival of a female in nearby branches brings a sudden chorus of harsh cries from the assembled males as they lower their wings and erect their golden plumes above their backs. If a female hops down to perch beside one of the males his dance becomes more passionate as he moves through several balletic phases, with the female, squatting and apparently impassive, close by. At the climax of his performance, which may take less than a minute, the chosen male leaps on the female's back and, as is the way with birds, copulates within a second or so. After that the female flies away and will not return that season.

Does she really, when she arrives, assess all the males individually to pick her winner? Or does she choose the one who is performing on one particular perch? The fact is that the great majority of copulations in a display tree take place with one single male, the possessor of a perch that seems to be particularly favoured. Males compete for perches by physical fighting and by displaying their plumes. So differences in plume quality may also be significant to other males as well as to females.

These massed displays are performed not only by all species of the genus *Paradisaea* (except for the Blue Bird) but also by the Standardwing and all *Astrapia* species. Such assemblies are known among ornithologists as 'leks', a Swedish term they originally used for the assemblages of male ruffs, small wading birds that gather and display in similar competitive groups on Scandinavian seashores.

It might seem that a male *Parotia*, pirouetting alone on his carefully prepared arena on the ground, has adopted a rather different tactic for attracting a female. But he is not as isolated as he seems. *Parotia* arenas, scattered through the forest, in fact form a coherent group. Each of them is within earshot of a neighbour, so it is easy for a female to tour from one arena to another in order to assess the quality of rival males.

(*Facing page*). Arfak Six-wired Bird of Paradise, male. Jacques Barraband, *c.*1800. Watercolour, 52 cm x 38 cm (21 in x 15 in). Private collection.

(*Page 214*). Male Brown Sicklebill displaying to a female. W. T. Cooper, 1989. Acrylic on panel, 102 cm x 69 cm (40 in x 27 in). Private collection.

(*Page 215*). Male Magnificent Bird of Paradise displaying to a female. W. T. Cooper, *c.*1990. Acrylic on panel, 81 cm x 71 cm (32 in x 28 in). Private collection.

Ornithologists call this kind of grouping an 'exploded lek', though the term is perhaps unfortunate since it implies that the arrangement is derived from a normal lek, whereas it is just as likely to be the other way round.

It is possible that the King Bird too uses an exploded lek, though the evidence is not conclusive. The males of other spectacular species – the Magnificent, the King of Saxony, the Superb, the Twelve-wired and the four Sicklebills – all display individually without reference to their rivals. The female must then travel around the forest, assessing which of them has the best-kept arena, the most varied vocal repertoire and the most brilliant and exciting plumage.

A cameraman filming bird of paradise display will of course wish to complete his sequence with a shot of the copulation. Things are comparatively easy for him when filming a massed lek like that of the Greater Bird. If he sees one copulation but fails to focus his camera on it before it finishes, he need not be concerned. All he has to do is to keep his camera trained on that particular branch and the next female to arrive at the lek will almost certainly make for the same place and be mated by the same male.

Things are not so easy when filming species that have exploded leks or inde-pendent ones. If the cameraman is wise and has the chance, he will inspect other display grounds in the neighbourhood

and choose the one that seems to him to be the best kept by the smartest-looking male. If he picks the wrong one, he will be almost as disappointed as the male bird himself.

Male birds spend most of their year close by the site where they display. A female, however, once she has mated, has to leave for she has to lay her eggs and rear her chicks. And since her momentary partner is still strutting his stuff on his display ground, she has to do all that entirely by herself.

It follows, therefore, that such polygamous systems can only develop in places where there is plenty of food easily available. And that is indeed the case in the New Guinea forests. All birds of paradise feed on fruit. Most supplement that with insects, but fruit of some sort is the most important element and that is available throughout the year.

The system also has a consequence for the male – a consequence that ultimately transfigures him. If a young male appears who is marginally better endowed than his fellows – with the colour or size of plumes that the local females prefer – then the genes that gave him that characteristic will quickly spread through the local population. And this will take place more swiftly than if the gene responsible becomes submerged in the next generation among those of other breeding males in the neighbourhood. If the females maintain their preference for this quality, year after year, then these decorations will become even more exaggerated, generation after generation, as the local champion maintains his exclusive access to the females and denies any competing males a place in the local gene pool. Evolutionists call this snow-balling effect 'runaway sexual selection'. And it is this that has led to male birds of paradise acquiring such outsized and bizarre plumes, even though these plumes may in practice be a handicap from many points of view.

Males do not, however, acquire their plumes until they are several years old – seven in the case of the Greater and Lesser Birds. Until that time, they look very like the females of their species. What is more, young unplumed males frequently spend some time around a lek, watching what goes on and, presumably, learning the dances being performed by their elders. They look so like females that occasionally a plumed male will attempt to mate with one of these young bachelors under the impression, clearly, that they really are of the opposite sex.

Count Raggi's Bird of Paradise, male and female. W. T. Cooper, 1981. Watercolour, 60 cm x 45 cm (24 in x 18 in). Private collection.

(*Facing page*). Four images each showing a male bird in a transitional stage of plumage development. Males begin with feathering like that of a female and pass through several stages before acquiring full adult plumage.

(*Top, left*). King Birds of Paradise, two adult males and an immature developing tail decoration, with a female. Hand-coloured lithograph by Joseph Wolf and Joseph Smit from D. G. Elliot's *Monograph of the Paradiseidae* (1873).
(*Top, right*). Lesser Birds of Paradise, a female with an immature male growing extended tail wires. Hand-coloured lithograph by William Hart from R. Bowdler Sharpe's *Monograph of the Paradiseidae* (1891–98).
(*Bottom, left*). Paradise Riflebirds, male and female, with an immature male showing incomplete breast shield and undeveloped feathers of head and stomach. Hand-coloured lithograph by William Hart from R. Bowdler Sharpe's *Monograph of the Paradiseidae* (1891–98).
(*Bottom, right*). Twelve-wired Birds of Paradise, two females and an immature male that lacks ornamental wires and shows the barred underside typical of a female. Hand-coloured lithograph by William Hart and John Gould from Gould's *Birds of New Guinea* (1875–88).

(*This page*). Sexual displays of birds of paradise fancifully imagined by someone who never saw them. A nineteenth-century engraving of a Lesser Bird (derived from Wolf's depiction – *see page 63*) displaying with a King, by an unknown artist, from J. G. Wood's *Illustrated Natural History* (1872). The third bird appears to be an immature Lesser Bird.

It also seems equally likely that plumed males, especially perhaps those that are sexually frustrated by the mating monopoly of the dominant male in the lek, will pounce on a female of another closely related species should she appear beside a display ground. Since the species in the family are, in spite of the difference in the plumage of the males, closely related, these 'illicit' couplings stand a chance of producing fertile offspring – hybrids.

11

Hybrids

Hybrids

It is a general conception that there should be no such thing as a hybrid. Species are often regarded as fixed types that breed only within their own populations, 'each after its own kind', in the biblical phrase. For the most part that is what they do, and it is commonly thought that a member of one species will have no wish to mate with a member of another. Even if a mating does occur, it is usually supposed that there will be insuperable physical barriers preventing any successful outcome in terms of offspring. Yet this belief is not reflected in reality, and hybridisation between species certainly does occur. While it may not be particularly common, hybridisation is one of the mechanisms of evolution and it is by no means as rare as might be imagined. It occurs in plants, it occurs in mammals, and it occurs in birds. There is no doubt that it usually takes some kind of special or peculiar circumstance to bring it into effect. But the special circumstances can be many and various and are not necessarily just a question of one individual having no access to others of its kind. As far as birds are concerned, some families (often those that are sexually dimorphic and have polygamous breeding systems) seem more prone to hybridisation than others. The hummingbirds, the ducks and the pheasants are all susceptible to this kind of promiscuous behaviour. And so, of course, are the birds of paradise. Hybrids, however, can often go unnoticed, and it sometimes takes special circumstances to bring them to light.

When the plume trade was at its height, unimaginable numbers of skins and feathers of birds of paradise were sent to Europe and North America every year. These items of commerce came from birds killed by Papuan plume hunters and delivered to merchants in various parts of what is now Indonesia who then forwarded them to Paris, London, Amsterdam, Berlin or New York. Every so often, in among the bundles

(Previous two pages (details) *and facing page).* 'Paradisaea mixta', a male hybrid between the Greater Bird of Paradise and the Lesser, with a female Greater Bird. This hybrid shows the velvet brown breast pad of the Greater and the Lesser's yellow flash on the wing. Errol Fuller, *c.*1992. Oils on panel, 55 cm x 42 cm (22 in x 17 in). Private collection.

of skins of the more familiar kinds, specimens occurred (most with no locality data other than that they came from New Guinea) with plumage than didn't conform to any of the standard patterns.

Were these new, previously unknown, species? Keen-eyed merchants – anxious to maximise their profits – spotted them and sold them at high prices to museums and wealthy private collectors. It was confidently expected that in due course many similar birds would turn up, and that their home grounds would eventually be identified. After all, legitimate new species were being discovered regularly, so there was no reason to suspect that some of these new finds weren't quite what they seemed. Meanwhile, scientific names were given to each of these new forms and – widely accepted as legitimate species – they passed into ornithological literature.

Some of these mysterious new birds of paradise turned up by the plume trade were very spectacular indeed. Take, for example, Wilhelmina's Bird of Paradise, or *Lamprothorax wilhelminae* as it was scientifically christened. With a tuft of black feathers at the base of its beak, a purple head and glorious blue breast shield, a cape on its shoulders and two long central retrices of metallic blue, it was named in all its regal splendour, during 1894, after Wilhelmina, then queen of Holland. It was quite unlike any known bird, but with only three specimens (today divided among museums in Leiden, Dresden and New York) having ever been found, was it exactly what it seemed?

As the years went by and the plume trade passed into history, it became apparent that none of these new forms, such as Wilhelmina's, was being observed in the wild. Suspicions began to be voiced that some might be excessively rare simply because they had a hybrid origin.

At this time there was little appreciation of just how close relationships were between species in the family. Among birds of paradise, there are such astonishing and striking varieties of plumage that ornithologists tended to believe that there were considerable distances between them. In addition, it was not yet realised that the breeding systems adopted by the birds might actually encourage the occasional production of hybrids between species. In fact the breeding systems were virtually unknown; few Europeans or Americans had even seen living birds. Determinations were, therefore, being made almost exclusively from evaluations of dried museum specimens, with little or no background information.

Wilhelmina's Bird of Paradise, a hybrid between the Superb Bird and the Magnificent. Hand-coloured lithograph by Bruno Geisler from *Abhandlungen und Berichte des Koniglichen Zoologischen Museum zur Dresden* (1894–95).

During the late 1920s the distinguished German ornithologist Erwin Stresemann decided to re-evaluate all the anomalous forms that were known only from excessively rare museum specimens. Stresemann had spent some time among the islands of the South Pacific, but there was only one place to begin his evaluation – and that place was far from New Guinea.

He arranged to visit Lord Rothschild's private museum at Tring in Hertfordshire, England. Stresemann had a certain amount of contempt for Walter Rothschild who, despite his enormous enthusiasm and zeal as a collector, had no formal qualification in the area of hard science. This, however, is where Stresemann felt he personally excelled. Yet in order to conduct his research Stresemann needed Rothschild desperately, for at that time Walter's private collection contained more kinds of birds of paradise, including the rare ones, than any other museum. Despite Stresemann's contempt, which must have been apparent, Rothschild generously allowed the German professor to stay in his house and have the run of his collection. Here Stresemann was able to assemble long series of skins and compare and contrast them, carefully noting plumage similarities and differences.

Having concluded his study, Stresemann once again turned to Rothschild for help, and the article announcing his findings was published in Walter's own scientific journal *Novitates Zoologicae* during 1930. It was written in German and titled *Welche Paradiesvogelarten der Literatur sind Hybriden Ursprungs?* (which translates as 'Which Birds of Paradise listed in the literature are of Hybrid Origin').

Stresemann had come to the conclusion that no less than 17 of the 'rare' forms were not legitimate species, but were hybrids. He proposed that they were the result of crosses between better-known kinds, and he suggested a parentage for each one.

There need be no doubt about most of his designations. They are correct, and the ornithological world immediately accepted them as such. At a stroke 17 species were struck from the records, and they have remained so.

However, despite the value and truth of most of his decisions, the learned paper that Stresemann produced to announce his findings was couched in very cryptic terms. Many ornithologists have assumed it to be satisfactory in all respects without ever having actually read it, yet it has a number of inadequacies.

Even one of Stresemann's closest associates became confused. His celebrated pupil, the evolutionary biologist Ernst Mayr (1904–2005) – renowned for his thoroughness and methodical approach – gave his old teacher full support, yet proceeded to create an entirely new genus,

Astrapimachus, for a bird he believed to be a hybrid (for a picture of this bird *see page 155*).

One voice in particular was raised in protest. An Australian museum worker named Tom Iredale (1880–1972) questioned Stresemann's determinations, but his books, *Birds of Paradise and Bower Birds* and its follow-up *Birds of New Guinea*, both published in Australia during the early 1950s, are so eccentric that they have largely been ignored.

The influential American bird of paradise expert Ernest Thomas Gilliard (1912–1965) also expressed reservations. But he died suddenly and prematurely and never finished his researches, and his authoritative work, also titled *Birds of Paradise and Bower Birds* (1969), was published posthumously.

The fact is that, despite any shortcomings in his paper, Stresemann's findings have survived the test of time. Not only has none of the birds he discussed ever been found in the wild, but there are now many arguments concerning habits and behavioural patterns that can be advanced to support the likelihood of hybridisation within the family. Several species have actually been observed to hybridise and produce forms that were entirely unknown in Stresemann's time.

Princess Stephanie's Astrapia, for instance, has been seen to cross with the Ribbon-tailed Bird of Paradise in a hybrid zone where the two species come into contact. This zone was found at Yanka in the Central Highlands by Fred Shaw Mayer, the man who was so instrumental in the initial discovery of the Ribbon-tail itself.

The offspring are fertile and can cross back with either of their parent species, resulting in a variety of plumages, some of which are approximately intermediate, others of which tend towards one parent or the other. This hybrid, in its various forms, has become known as Barnes' Astrapia.

Various combinations of plume bird are known from museum specimens, and the form known as *Paradisaea mixta* (*see page 223*) is a good example. But they are not just known from dried specimens in museums; hybrid zones, just like the one in which Barnes' Astrapia occurs, have occasionally been found in the wild, and subtle variations in plumage occur.

Barne's Astrapia, male. Errol Fuller, 1993. Oils on panel, 28 cm x 13 cm (11 in x 5 in). Private collection.

One of the more interesting of the birds dismissed by Stresemann as a hybrid is called Duivenbode's Riflebird, after the merchant who first brought it to attention. Originally given the rather glorious scientific name of *Paryphephorus duivenbodei*, it is known from just three museum specimens (one of which exists at the Tring Museum, another at the American Museum of Natural History, New York, and a third which was once in Dresden, but which was lost during the upheavals caused by World War II). Curiously, there is some evidence that suggests that this form, although known only from these museum specimens, occurs in a specific hybrid zone. Unlike most of the excessively rare kinds discussed by Stresemann, there is specific locality data for the two specimens that are still in existence.

Stresemann alleged that the parent species are the Superb Bird and the Magnificent Riflebird, and the plumage evidence certainly suggests that this might be the case. Yet these two birds live at different levels in the forest – the Superb lives at heights well above those generally frequented by the Riflebird. It is, therefore, a curious fact that the two existing museum specimens were taken within just a kilometre or two of one another – yet 34 years apart – in the Owen Stanley Mountains of southeast New Guinea. One of them was actually collected by the same Fred Shaw Mayer who was responsible for locating the hybrid zone that produces Barnes' Astrapia.

Is there some special factor operating in this area that allows Superb Birds to descend to the territory of the Riflebird, or vice versa? Or perhaps the birds aren't hybrids after all but a legitimate species with a very restricted range?

The frequency of the production of hybrids like Barnes' Astrapia, and in particular the continuing viability of some of them, raises an interesting possibility. Is it feasible that in the right circumstances such hybridisation might eventually result in the creation of entirely new species? If the zone of overlap that allows the production of fertile hybrids became isolated from the terrain supporting its original parent species, then presumably the hybrids would continue to breed freely. In time they might evolve into a form very different from their originators. This in itself raises a curious possibility. Did any of the species we now recognise originate in such a way?

Since the time of Stresemann several additional hybrid forms have come to light. Perhaps the most interesting of these is a bird that has

Duivenbode's Riflebird. Hand-coloured lithograph by J. G. Keulemans from *Ibis* (1890).

come to be known as Captain Blood's Bird of Paradise. The spectacularly named Captain Neptune Newcombe Beresford Lloyd Blood (1907–?) was a patrol officer in the highlands of New Guinea during the 1940s and 1950s. During his time in the country, between rescuing downed World War II pilots from the Japanese war machine, discovering a new species of orchid and turning 8 ha (20 acres) of New Guinea into an English country garden, he collected many bird of paradise specimens that he sent to the Australian Museum in Sydney. Often he was accompanied on his expeditions in the Mount Hagen area by his very young blond-haired daughter, and on one of these expeditions he discovered a unique specimen – a bird that appears to be a cross between the Blue Bird and Count Raggi's.

Long before Stresemann's time, or Captain Blood's, Jacques Barraband produced some very mysterious watercolours among the illustrations that he painted of more familiar birds of paradise. Two show an individual, or individuals, that are very close in appearance to Twelve-wired birds (*see pages 80 and 81*), but another is similarly enigmatic. It shows an individual that seems to be either an immature or a female of a plume bird species, but it reveals a colour pattern that is quite untypical. It could be a freak, it could be a hybrid.

These are not the only mysteries, however. Among Stresemann's designations are three that stand out as particularly unsatisfactory. One of these, Elliot's Bird of Paradise, is discussed in Chapter 6: Sicklebills. Another was given the name *Loborhamphus nobilis*, the Noble Lobe-bill. Known from just two museum specimens, both now in the American Museum of Natural History in New York, this strange creature was considered by Stresemann to result from matings between the Superb Bird and the Long-tailed Paradigalla. But the combination of features that the two known specimens show is too complex to unravel so glibly. No completely convincing conclusion can be reached from a study of the plumage evidence alone, and any two species selected at random from a dozen or so could be nominated as putative parents. Stresemann's conclusion is no more than a guess, an attempt to force an enigma into a shape that fits a theory. He may be right, of course, but on ethological grounds alone the pairing seems unlikely. There is no particularly close relationship between the proposed parents, and in appearance the sexes of *Paradigalla* are virtually identical, while those of the Superb Bird are entirely different. While this in itself would not make a crossing impossible, it certainly makes it rather unlikely.

(*Above*). Captain Blood's Bird of Paradise. Errol Fuller, 1993. Oils on panel, 35 cm x 25 cm (14 in x 10 in). Private collection.

(*Facing page*). A curiously plumed immature bird that bears some relationship to a Lesser Bird of Paradise. Jacques Barraband, *c*.1800. Watercolour, 52 cm x 38 cm (21 in x 15 in). Private collection.

J. Grönvold.

Equally unsatisfactory is the case of the bird known as Bensbach's Bird of Paradise. Originally named *Janthothorax bensbachi*, it is known from a unique specimen in the Leiden Museum. Stresemann decided that this specimen resulted from the illicit mating of a Lesser Bird of Paradise with a Magnificent Riflebird.

(*Facing page*). The Noble Lobe-bill, a hybrid or a lost species? Hand-coloured lithograph by H. Gronvold from *Novitates Zoologicae* (1903).

(*This page*). Bensbach's Bird of Paradise, perhaps a hybrid between the Lesser Bird of Paradise and the Magnificent Riflebird – or perhaps not. Hand-coloured lithograph by J. G. Keulemans and W. Hart (after a painting by Keulemans) from R. Bowdler Sharpe's *Monograph of the Paradiseidae* (1891–98).

His explanation for this assumption was brief, and extraordinary:

*Vollig geschwarzte Untersite und die Qualität des
Schillers an verschiedenen Regionen des Gefieders
schliessen* Seleucides *aus und zeugen für* Ptiloris.

(Completely blackened undersides and the quality
of shimmer in various parts of the plumage, exclude
Seleucides [Twelve-wired Bird] and point to *Ptiloris*
[Magnificent Riflebird]).

Quite why blackened underparts should prove the guilt of the
Magnificent Riflebird is unclear; no less than 20 other bird of paradise
species show this particular characteristic. The remarks about quality
of shimmer are no more enlightening; one of the trademarks of birds
of paradise is their beautiful array of sheens and glosses. The single
individual now part of the collection of the Leiden Museum may or may
not be a hybrid, but it is truly an enigma.

But ornithology has moved on, and the argument is now largely
academic. Stresemann's masterpiece of ornithological detection might
have balanced perfectly had he not pursued his well-conceived general
hypothesis to a positive conclusion in each individual case. That the birds
of paradise hybridise to a degree that is not typical of birds in general
cannot be doubted. Whether all of Stresemann's designations are as
accurate as they have been held to be is another matter.

Eventually, advanced methods of analysing museum specimen tissue
may provide conclusive evidence of whether or not New Guinea's forests
still harbour species additional to those we already know of in the most
spectacular bird family in the world. Who knows?

The earliest-known picture of
an anomalous bird of paradise,
showing plumage that conforms
to that of no known species.
Attributed to Zacharius Wehme,
*c.*1590. Watercolour and body
colour on paper, 51 cm x 29 cm
(20 in x 11½ in). Staatliche
Kunstsammlungen, Dresden.

People Associated with the Discovery and Visual Representation of Birds of Paradise

This appendix is somewhat arbitrary and by no means comprehensive, and not all of the people mentioned in the book are listed. Where a portrait of an individual has been found, it is included. The size at which such images are reproduced – or even their inclusion – is not intended as a reflection of a person's importance in the story of the birds of paradise.

Ulysses Aldrovandus (1522–1605). Although he was professor of medicine at the University of Bologna, Aldrovandus was deeply interested in all aspects of the natural world and throughout his long life he collected specimens of everything he could find. Eventually, his collection was said to fill over 4,000 drawers. In 1599, at the age of 77, he started to publish accounts and illustrations of the specimens he possessed – and many, including dragons and mermaids, that he did not. Much of his information was based on a previous work written by a Swiss scholar, Conrad Gesner (1516–65). But whereas Gesner had arranged his entries alphabetically, Aldrovandus recognised the relationships between animals and grouped them, more scientifically, in families. He died in 1605 with only three volumes of his work, *The Ornithologiae*, completed. His pupils, however, continued his work, at first using his notes and then compiling the information themselves. The last of the 13 volumes of this great encyclopaedia appeared in 1667 over 60 years after its founder's death.

Jacques Barraband (1761–1809). Despite the incredible beauty of his images, and the great influence they have had, comparatively little is known of Jacques Barraband, and it has not proved possible to find a portrait of him. He was the son of a weaver, and it seems that he worked originally as a tapestry designer at Gobelin's, and later turned his hand to decorating porcelain at the famous factory in Sèvres. In his late twenties he came to the attention of François Levaillant who commissioned him to paint watercolours (to be used as the basis for engravings from which book illustrations were produced) of birds – mostly toucans, parrots, cotingas, rollers and birds of paradise. These watercolours stand among the finest paintings of birds ever produced. Barraband died at a comparatively young age in Lyon.

Captain Neptune Newcombe Beresford Lloyd Blood (1907–78?) (pictured with his daughter second from left, and inset) is something of a man of mystery. Even the date of his death remains uncertain. His daughter recalled him as a modest man who thought little of his exploits, yet he was responsible for saving many servicemen from the rigours of New Guinea's jungles during World War II. He made several important contributions to ornithology and botany during his New Guinea patrols in the 1940s and 1950s.

Charles Lucien Bonaparte (1803–57) was a nephew of Napoleon, and he spent much time in America where he championed John James Audubon. His great love was natural history but he was unable to shake off the family association with politics. A great supporter of democracy, he took part in various revolutionary activities and found time to father 12 children.

Raymond Ching (1939–) is widely acclaimed as one of the world's most accomplished painters; natural history pictures are only part of his artistic repertoire. A New Zealander by birth, he has maintained studios in both his home country and in England, and his paintings have been exhibited in many parts of the world. Despite the wide range of his subject matter, birds of paradise are among his earliest and greatest interests.

William Cooper (1934–).
Australian born and bred, he began his career as a landscape painter but in 1968 he produced *A Portfolio of Australian Birds*, which immediately put him on the foremost rank of bird painters. Soon he took on the tradition established by John Gould and started to produce large-folio volumes containing paintings of all the species of a particular family, together with a text written by a taxonomist. His plates of birds of paradise, with texts by Joseph Forshaw, were published in 1977, but he has also produced equally

authoritative and spectacular volumes on parrots, kingfishers, hornbills, and turacos. He lives with his botanist wife, Wendy, and paints birds, surrounded by the rainforest of northern Queensland.

Carolus Clusius (1526–1609).
Charles Lecluse, to give him his un-Latinised name, became Prefect of the Imperial Viennese Medical Garden in 1573, but his natural history interests were broad and he had access to the emperor's cabinet of curiosities. There he saw a bird of paradise skin and realised that the stories of the birds' leglessness were mere myths. In 1593 he became a professor at Leiden University and established one of the first scientifically organised botanic gardens. But he also regularly visited docks to check on curiosities being brought back by ships from the east. As a horticulturalist, he became expert in breeding tulips with streaked and feathered petals and so became a key figure in the 'tulipomania' that swept western Europe in the 1600s.

Lee Crandall (1887–1969).
For many years Lee Crandall was the curator of the Bronx Zoo, New York, and was responsible for many innovations at that institution. His interest in birds of paradise resulted in his celebrated field trip to New Guinea during the 1920s, and the interesting book, *Paradise Quest*, which details his exploits. Subsequently, Crandall made observations of several species displaying in captivity, and for many years these observations were the only ones of their kind. Even today, they are still quoted. When asked why he was so interested in birds, Crandall always gave the same answer – 'I don't know'.

Luigi Maria D'Albertis (1841–1901) was a flamboyant Italian aristocrat who made significant contributions to the exploration of New Guinea. His most celebrated New Guinea adventure was to steam up the River Fly, for a distance of almost 1,000 km (600 miles), in a launch called the *Neva*. The voyage was an eccentric one, and included such acts as letting off fireworks to scare away hostile natives, engaging in pitch battles when such actions didn't work, and keeping a pet snake on board to inhibit the pilfering of supplies. Weariness and ill health led to his return to Italy with important collections of natural history and ethnographical material. He retired to Rome where he lived alone, and died from cancer of the mouth. He once remarked that in his opinion it was easier to cross the Alps than to ascend an ordinary hill in Papua.

François Daudin (1774–1804). Despite having legs paralysed by a childhood disease, François Daudin excelled in physics and natural history. He became an expert in ornithology and the study of reptiles and amphibians. Although he published several important books during his short life, these were commercial failures, and he and his wife lived in poverty. She died of tuberculosis and he followed her less than a year later.

Daniel Giraud Elliot (1835–1915) had both a passion for birds and a great deal of money. He assembled one of the finest collections of bird skins in private hands. This was eventually acquired by the American Museum of Natural History, New York, of which he was one of the founders. He finished his scientific career as keeper of ornithology at the Field Museum in Chicago. He was both a competent artist and a lover of fine books and was determined to follow the fashion established by John Gould, and if possible improve upon it. He published his first book, on Pittas or Ant-Thrushes, in 1861 and illustrated it with his own drawings and others by Paul Louis Oudart. Then followed two other even larger volumes – on grouse, and a collection of previously un-illustrated North American birds in which his own work was once again supplemented by others, including the great Joseph Wolf. Next he tackled pheasants. And then the birds of paradise. The plates for these were once again drawn by Joseph Wolf. The volume on birds of paradise contains 37 hand-coloured plates, each *c.* 60 cm x 45 cm (24 in x 18 in) when trimmed for binding – a size known as elephant folio. It must count as one of the most sumptuous of illustrated bird books, and Elliot, very appropriately, dedicated it to Alfred Russel Wallace.

Errol Flynn (1909–59). Adventurer, bar-fly, beachcomber, boxer, brawler, drifter, entertainer, freedom fighter, lover, platypus and bird fancier, prospector, self-confessed thief, sailor, writer, Hollywood icon, Errol Flynn packed almost every conceivable human activity into his whirlwind tour through life. He starred in almost 60 films, wrote two novels and an autobiography, before dying at the comparatively early age of 50 from the effects of a totally worn-out body.

Bruno Geisler (1857–1945) collected birds and ethnographical artefacts in New Guinea and other parts of the South Pacific, mainly for the Dresden Museum. He became the museum's taxidermist but is best known for the paintings of birds that he produced for several important German publications.

John Gould (1804–81), the son of a gardener working at Windsor Castle, was in 1827 appointed curator at the newly formed Zoological Society of London with the responsibility for preserving and mounting the bodies of many of the animals that died in the Society's gardens – the London Zoo. While there, he began publishing illustrations of some of the birds whose skins were sent to the Society for classification. Initially, these were drawn by his wife, Elizabeth, and she continued as his principal artist for ten years thereafter. She died in 1841 at the age of 37, after giving birth to their eighth child. Gould, now operating as an independent publisher, engaged a series of other artists to draw his plates. Eventually he produced just one short of 3,000 of them. His work of classifying and often naming species gave him a considerable reputation as a taxonomist, and he was called upon to pronounce on whether the different specimens of finches brought back by Darwin from the Galapagos were in fact separate species or just local variants. Perhaps the least of his talents was the one with which he is most widely credited – painting birds.

(*Facing page*). John Gould with a specimen of Count Raggi's Bird of Paradise. Two paintings of birds of paradise, perhaps preliminary studies, are pinned to the wall. H. R. Robertson, 1878. Oils on canvas, 127 cm x 101 cm (50 in x 40 in). Private collection.

Henrik Gronvold (1858–1940) was a Danish-born illustrator who travelled to Britain and, towards the end of the nineteenth century, took over the mantle of the great, but ageing, bird illustrators like Keulemans, Wolf and Hart. He particularly excelled at painting birds' eggs.

William Matthew Hart (1830–1908) produced a huge number of lithographic plates of birds, based on his watercolours and oils – many of them for John Gould – but little is known of him and he has received only limited credit for his efforts. Born in Ireland, he spent most of his life in Camberwell, south London, and he is buried in the cemetery there.

Jack Hides (1906–38). Between the two World Wars, in the 1920s and 1930s, the eastern half of New Guinea was administered by an extraordinary group of young Australians. Aged mostly in their twenties and thirties, they led locally recruited men, known as policemen (shown with Hides, *below*), on patrols lasting months through little-explored and often totally unknown country, full of people armed with spears and stone axes who did not necessarily welcome visitors. Jack Hides led one of the most daring. So proud were his men of their government positions, and so disciplined their conduct, that they were quite prepared to give their lives during these arduous expeditions. The dying words of one were, 'My light is going out, but it doesn't matter – I am wearing the judge's coat' – a reference to Judge Murray, then head of New Guinea administration. Hides published several interesting and revealing accounts of these explorations, including *Through Wildest Papua* (1935), *Papuan Wonderland* (1936) and *Savages in Serge* (1937). He then resigned from the public service, and in 1937 led an expedition prospecting for gold. Like many before him, he had no success, and, perhaps debilitated from all the hardships he had endured, he died from pneumonia soon after his return.

Joris Hoefnagel (1542–1601) and Jacob (1575–1630). Joris (George) Hoefnagel was a Flemish-born painter and engraver who travelled to make a living. In his twenties he was in England where he painted a well-known picture of a wedding at Bermondsey; he also produced an early map of London. Later, he spent time in Munich before working for Emperor Rudolf II in Prague and Vienna. His son Jacob carried on the family tradition, and it is not always certain which of the animal pictures produced for the emperor were by the father and which were by the son.

Carl Hunstein (1843–88). Leaving Germany as a young man Hunstein travelled to America and then New Zealand, before moving on to New Guinea in search of gold. This proved something of a failure, and he joined forces with fellow Germans in search of birds of paradise. He was enormously successful and discovered several new species, but died in a tsunami while searching for others. It is said that during seven years among hostile tribes, he never once had occasion to use violent means of defence – preferring other ways of avoiding trouble.

Tom Iredale (1880–1972). Raised near Workington close to the English Lake District, Tom Iredale travelled to New Zealand and then Australia where he pursued a career in museums, specialising in conchology and ornithology. He produced wildly eccentric books setting himself very much against ornithological orthodoxy. During the early 1950s his books on birds of paradise and the birds of New Guinea were made in conjunction with his wife, the painter Lilian Medland.

John Gerrard Keulemans (1842–1912) was an illustrator in Leyden when he came to the attention of Richard Bowdler Sharpe, who asked him to illustrate a book on kingfishers, and then persuaded him to settle in England. They worked closely together for the next 30 years. His work was soon sought after all over Europe for journals and books. The style changed little, with birds nearly always perched or at rest, and details of beaks, feet and plumage defined with meticulous accuracy, Foregrounds, leafy or rocky, are detailed and backgrounds fainter and more sketchy. His images were usually reproduced by lithography and often transferred to lithographic stone by Keulemans himself. He also provided such a service for other artists. In personality he was shy, polite, taciturn and withdrawn, totally absorbed, it seems, in his work.

Charles R. Knight (1874–1953).
Although famed for his iconic
and evocative images of
dinosaurs and other prehistoric
life, Knight regarded himself
primarily as a painter of living
animals and birds, and based his
restorations of fossil remains on a
lifelong study of extant creatures.
A close connection with the
Bronx Zoo and the animals that
were constantly arriving there
helped enormously in this.
Curiously, he was regarded as
legally 'blind' due to astigmatism
and an injury to his right eye.

John Latham (1740–1837) was born at Eltham, then in Kent, and started
working life as a medical doctor at nearby Dartford, but he had been fascinated
by birds as a child and he continued to collect and draw all the specimens he
could obtain. His medical practice flourished and earned him so much money
that he was able to devote himself to his ornithological studies. His ambition
was to list every bird known to science and where possible illustrate them with
engravings that for the most part he drew, engraved, printed and coloured
himself. His first publication, *A General Synopsis of Birds,* appeared in 1781. Five
more volumes followed in 1785 and further supplements in 1787 and 1801. By
this time his fortune was spent but he continued working, trying to keep pace
with the new species that were flooding into Britain as explorers opened up
the world. In 1801 he started on a new edition of his *Synopsis* which he called
A General History of Birds. It contained 193 plates and listed 3,000 species. He
continued drawing new species until just before his death in 1837 aged 97.

Reverend William Lawes (1839–1907)
of the London Missionary Society spent
much of his life at Port Moresby and
translated the New Testament into Motu,
the local language. A Six-wired bird of
paradise, *Parotia lawesii*, was named in
his honour.

René Primevère Lesson (1794–1849), served in a medical capacity aboard one of the French exploratory expeditions to the South Seas. His great interest in natural history led him to collect specimens and make observations of the animals and birds that he saw. He was the first European naturalist to see birds of paradise in the wild. On his return to France he published several books on natural history subjects including one on birds of paradise, *Histoire Naturelle des Oiseaux de Paradis et des Epimaques.*

François Levaillant (1753–1824), was born in Surinam (now the Republic of Suriname), studied in Europe, and made expeditions to Africa. Following these he wrote several lavish books, including a six-volume treatise on African birds, and he formed a collaboration with a number of artists, including Jacques Barraband, who painted hundreds of pictures for him. Levaillant went on to publish magnificent books on several bird families, but despite the sumptuous nature of these, he died in poverty.

Carl Linnaeus (1707–78). Carl von Linné, to use the Swedish version of his Latinised name, devised the system by which living organisms are given a universally recognised two-word scientific name. The first allocates an individual to a group of closely related organisms that he called a genus. *Paradisaea*, for example, is the generic name of closely related birds. The second name, such as *apoda*, defines the species to which a creature, in this case the Greater Bird of Paradise, belongs. Linnaeus, shown here in the dress of a Laplander, whose country he explored, was professor of medicine at Uppsala University, before he took the University's Chair of Botany.

Ferdinand Magellan (1480–1521). The celebrated expedition that Magellan commanded completed the first circumnavigation of the Earth. Setting sail from Spain and rounding Cape Horn into the Pacific, the expedition returned to Spain by way of the Cape of Good Hope. It is often stated that Magellan completed the circumnavigation himself. He didn't. He was killed during a battle in the Philippines, wounded first by a bamboo spear and finished off with other weapons. Only one of the five ships that originally set sail managed to return to Spain, and out of 237 men who had participated in the expedition, just 18 returned alive.

Lilian Medland (1880–1956), pictured with her husband Tom Iredale and their children Rex and Beryl, was born in Finchley, north London and, for the period, grew up to be a very independently minded woman, smoking and engaging in such activities as rearing lion cubs and raising salamanders. An attack of diphtheria when she was 27 left her deaf, but she continued to enjoy all sorts of outdoor activities. She moved to the Antipodes and married Tom Iredale – retaining her maiden name – later helping him with his various publishing projects and contributing illustrations. Her many paintings of birds of paradise – produced for his books – may lack technical finesse, but they have considerable charm.

Adolf Bernard Meyer (1840–1911) was instrumental in the development of the natural history museum at Dresden into one of the world's great collections. He showed particular interest in rare and curious forms and also in birds of the South Pacific, especially birds of paradise.

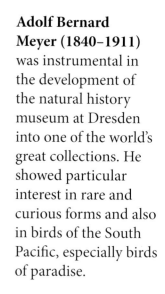

Alfred Newton (1829–1907) was a crusty yet highly respected professor of zoology, but he wrote surprisingly poetic passages on ornithological matters close to his heart. His pet subjects were the Great Auk and the Great Bustard. He wrote a ground-breaking *Dictionary of Birds*, and one of the great classics of ornithological literature, *Ootheca Wolleyana*.

Walter, 2nd Baron Rothschild (1868–1937), shown with his zebra and trap and (inset) with Albert Einstein and George Bernard Shaw. In his day Rothschild was one of the most remarkable figures in zoology. A scion of the celebrated banking house, he proved himself entirely unsuitable for the activities for which his family was famous. Instead, he turned his attention to natural history and formed a fantastic collection of specimens and associated items, as well as a magnificent library; he also founded and funded a scientific journal, *Novitates Zoologicae*. Blackmailed by a woman with whom he'd had an affair, he was eventually forced to sell much of his collection, including most of his beloved bird of paradise specimens.

Rudolf II, Holy Roman Emperor (1552–1612). Enthusiasm for art and science has been blamed for the political disasters of Rudolf's reign. Moving the Habsburg capital from Vienna to Prague in pursuit of his preoccupation, he made magnificent collections of paintings, sculpture, weapons, and all kinds of musical and scientific instruments, as well as living animals including birds. A long, indecisive war with the Turks ultimately led to his downfall. With no legitimate issue, he was stripped of power by his younger brother.

Rudolf, Crown Prince of Austria (1858–89). Son and heir of Franz Josef, Emperor of Austria, Hungary and Bohemia, Rudolf was destined to rule over the vast Austro-Hungarian Empire. But he quarrelled with his father over a number of issues and, apparently, committed suicide with his lover, Mary Vetsera, at a hunting lodge known as Mayerling. This set in motion a chain of events that ultimately brought about the end of the Habsburg Empire and the start of World War I.

Richard Bowdler Sharpe (1847–1909), is an interesting and unusual character in the history of nineteenth-century ornithology. From fairly modest beginnings worked his way up to a position of considerable prestige in the zoological world and produced a number of important books. He met John Gould, who had a profound influence on his life, while fishing near Cookham in Berkshire, and he met his wife while wandering in the woods there. The married couple went on to have no fewer than twelve daughters, some of whom helped very expertly with the hand-colouring of plates for his books. His happy home life was shattered when he died suddenly on Christmas Day in 1909.

Fred Shaw Mayer (1899–1989) is shown here holding his tame Pesquet's Parrot, a species which is found only in New Guinea. He was one of the last men to earn a living by collecting birds and animals and selling them, alive or dead, to museums and wealthy collectors. After working in many of the wilder parts of the Far East and the Pacific, he ended his career in charge of huge aviaries, full of birds of paradise, at Nondugl in the Wahgi Valley in the Central Highlands of New Guinea. The gardens there had been founded by Captain Neptune Blood, but the aviaries had been paid for by an Australian industrialist and bird enthusiast, Sir Edward Hallstrom, who intended that the birds should be sent to Taronga Park Zoo in Sydney, and to other zoos and parks in Europe. Eventually, however, Australian quarantine laws made exporting them impossible. Better known than Shaw-Mayer's tame parrot was a pet Count Raggi's Bird of Paradise which regularly performed displays for visitors to Nondugl. So popular did this bird become and so closely associated with Fred Shaw Mayer that it was known to those who saw it as 'Fred Raggiana'. When he finally entered a retirement home in Australia, two aviaries were built in the grounds so that he could continue looking after his birds.

Pierre Sonnerat (1748–1814), pictured on the frontispiece of his book *Voyage à la Nouvelle-Guinée,* was in many ways a ground-breaking naturalist and explorer. Yet many of his written observations need to be taken with a pinch of salt. Despite this qualification, his books are fascinating and full of interest. Setting out from France, he travelled several times to Southeast Asia, and on to China, the Philippines and the Moluccas. He also visited Madagascar. He held some remarkably modern views on a number of matters, including the subject of racism. Being particularly impressed with the various cultures of India, he regarded the Brahmins as the most enlightened of all human beings.

Princess Stephanie (1864–1945). A Belgian princess by birth, she married Crown Prince Rudolph when she was just sixteen, and expected that one day she would rule over the Austro-Hungarian Empire. However, she was widowed when Rudolph committed suicide at Mayerling. Before this tragedy, the royal pair had birds of paradise named after them and Stephanie's was a newly discovered *Astrapia*. After Rudolph's death Stephanie married a Hungarian count – apparently appalling certain members of European aristocracy who thought the marriage was beneath her. In her later years she wrote an autobiography titled *I Was To Be Empress*.

Samuel Stevens (1817–99). Little is known of Stevens, and had he not operated as Alfred Wallace's agent his name would have faded into history. However, he opened a natural history agency in London during 1848, one of his specialities being slides for the microscope, the material for which was sometimes obtained from Wallace and his fellow explorer Henry Bates. Doubtless, he handled the sale of many of the bird of paradise skins that Wallace sent back from his travels.

Erwin Stresemann (1889–1972), pictured being tattooed with the sign of the headhunter in Ceram during 1911, was born in Dresden of wealthy parents and travelled widely as a young man. He settled to become Curator of Birds at the Berlin Museum and one of the most distinguished ornithologists of his day. His most lasting achievement is the compilation of the *Aves* volume for the *Handbuch der Zoologie*, but perhaps of more interest to the general reader is his book *Ornithology from Aristotle to the Present*. His influence over a younger generation of evolutionary biologists was huge, and such was his prestige that after World War II he was allowed to travel freely through the divided city of Berlin from his home on the west side to the museum – which was in the eastern sector.

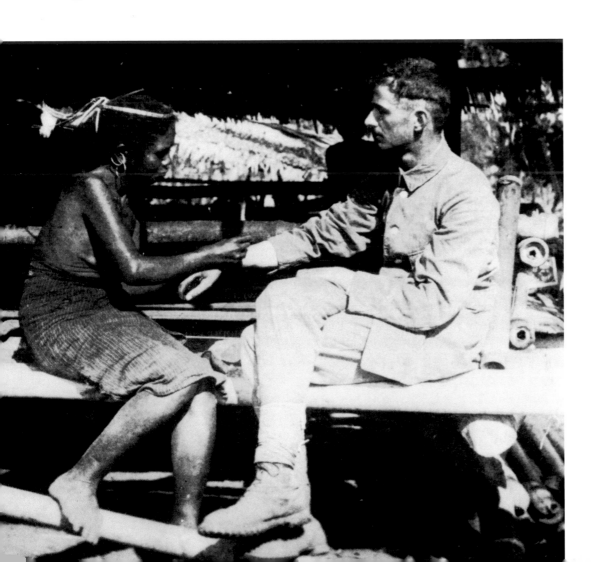

Carola Vasa (1833–1907), Queen of Saxony. As a young girl, Carola was considered one of the most beautiful of the royal princesses of Europe. A descendant of a deposed Swedish king, she married Albert of Saxony (with whom she is pictured), and became the last Queen of Saxony. Due to Saxony's connection (through the Dresden Museum) with the discovery of birds of paradise, both she and her husband gave their names to new species. *Pteridophora alberti* was named after the king, and is still popularly known as the King of Saxony's Bird of Paradise, and *Parotia carolae* is still called Queen Carola's Six-wired Bird. She interested herself in social issues and became an ardent supporter of nursing and the women's movement. Among other good works, she founded homes for the sick and handicapped.

Alfred Russel Wallace (1823–1913). Wallace's fame as a scientist rests primarily and justly on his co-authorship with Charles Darwin of the theory of evolution by natural selection that had occurred to him during a malarial fever when he was pursuing birds of paradise in eastern Indonesia. Far from resenting the fact that the theory became identified primarily with Darwin, he recognised that this was only just since Darwin had already assembled a huge mass of supporting evidence.

Wallace left school aged 14, but he was already fascinated by the natural world. After a few years spent assisting his brother as a surveyor and teaching at a school in Leicester, he left Britain to start exploring the tropics, first in Brazil and then Indonesia. He paid his way by sending batches of natural history specimens back to Europe where they were sold by his agent to wealthy enthusiasts. During his Indonesian journey he collected and prepared over 125,000 specimens. When, after eight years, he himself returned, he brought with him two living Lesser Birds of Paradise that he had purchased in Singapore. These he sold to the London Zoo for £300 plus free entry to the zoo. They may have been the first living birds of paradise to reach Europe, except for one that had been kept by the royal family at Windsor and had died 40 years earlier. During his last years he devoted himself to writing works not only on biogeography but on social issues such as land nationalisation and female suffrage, both of which he vigorously supported. He died, greatly honoured, aged 90.

Walter Weber (1906–76). Born in Chicago, one of eleven children, Walter Weber once exchanged a hundred of his drawings for a bottle of soda pop. His fortunes changed, however, and in 1949 he became staff artist and naturalist for *National Geographic* magazine, and it was for this organisation that he produced his influential images of birds of paradise.

Joseph Wolf (1820–99). German born, Wolf moved to Britain during his late twenties and stayed for the rest of his life. He became one of the most acclaimed animal and bird painters of his era, and his work was sought after by wealthy collectors and publishers alike. Even the great artist Edwin Landseer admired him and once said that he must have been a bird before he became a man! His favourite subjects were, perhaps, birds of prey, but his illustrations of birds of paradise were among his finest achievements.

Acknowledgements

Anyone writing about birds of paradise these days will, knowingly or unknowingly, owe a debt to Clifford Frith. The authors of this book certainly do. Together with Bruce Beehler, Frith has written the most modern and authoritative ornithological text about the family, *The Birds of Paradise* (1998). With his wife Dawn he has also made an encyclopaedic survey of the birds' cultural impact in *Birds of Paradise: Nature, Art and History* (2010).

We also have debts for help in the selection of the illustrations that are such a major element in this book. Head of the list must be Raymond Ching and William Cooper who both generously gave us free access to their work. Dr and Mrs Edelstone put us on the trail of material relating to John Gould, and Judith Magee guided us towards some of the treasures in her charge at the Natural History Museum, London. Sheikh Saud Al-Thani kindly allowed access to paintings by Jacques Barraband. Vaso Kafkoula, Carel Brest van Kempen, Rhoda Kalt Knight, Stephen Rose, and the Yale Centre for British Art generously permitted reproduction of artworks. Richard Milner and Catherine Wallis made very useful suggestions, and Roddy Paine and his colleague Gavin Sawyer helped with photography, as did Mark Wood. Michael Drew, Georgina and Tom Luck, Alan Peacock, Angi and Phil O'Neill, Sue Luck, Tess Fuller, Cirel Greenwell and Hugh Porter advised on technical matters. Finally, we are both indebted to Susan Attenborough who supported us in many ways and who thought of the book's title. Our sincere thanks go to them all.

D. F. A. & E. F.

Count Raggi's and Lesser Birds of Paradise. Stephen Rose, 2012. Oils on canvas, 57 cm x 71 cm (22 in x 27 in). Private collection.

Index

One of my objects in coming was accomplished. I had obtained a specimen of the King Bird of Paradise…. The remote island in which I found myself… in an almost unvisited sea, far from the tracks of merchant-fleets… the wild luxuriant tropical forest, which stretched far away on every side; the savages who gathered round… all had their influence in determining the emotions with which I gazed upon this 'thing of beauty'. I thought of the long ages of the past, during which successive generations of this little creature had run their course… being born, and living and dying amid these dark and gloomy woods, with no… eye to gaze upon their loveliness…. . It seems sad that… such exquisite creatures should live out their lives and exhibit their charms only in these wild inhospitable regions, doomed for ages yet to come to hopeless barbarism… [yet] should civilized man ever reach these distant lands, and bring… light into the recesses of these virgin forests, we may be sure that he will so disturb the nicely-balanced relations… of nature as to cause the disappearance, and finally the extinction, of these very beings whose… beauty he… is fitted to appreciate and enjoy. This consideration must surely tell us that all living things were not made for man. Many… have no relation to him. The cycle of their existence has gone on independently of his… and their happiness and enjoyment, their loves and hates, their struggles for existence, their vigorous life and early death, would seem to be immediately related to their own well-being and perpetuation alone, limited only by the equal well-being and perpetuation of the numberless other organisms with which each is more or less intimately connected.

Alfred Russel Wallace, 1869, *The Malay Archipelago.*